D0198638

£1·25

By The Harvest Moon

REMEMBER, remember that magic
   night,
   When romance and love were new?
The harvest moon lit up your hair,
   And captured your eyes of blue.

Remember, remember I kissed your lips
   And asked you to be my wife?
You hugged me tight, you answered,
   "Yes,"
   And promised to share my life.

Remember, remember — of course you
   do.
   How swiftly the days have fled!
But love has sweetened every hour,
   Since that vital word was said.

   Violet Hall.

People's Friend Annual

CONTENTS

SCENIC VIEWS   J. Campbell Kerr

BACK COVER   Buchaille Etive Mor from White Corries, Argyllshire

THE patchwork bedspread was a magnificent piece of work. Seven hundred and twenty small bits of material had been sewn together to make an unusual and colourful covering, and it was seen to its best advantage that Saturday as it lay on an old Victorian bed.

It was the local minister who had organised the exhibition in the church hall. There was no doubt it was his enthusiasm which had made it such a success.

"Bring along anything at all over fifty years old," he had told people. "The older the better! Everyone is so interested in antiques now, and good care will be taken of your possessions."

The Victorian bed had come from the manse itself. The beautiful blue and gold china belonged to old Miss Carlyle of Beech House, and the child's wooden cradle was owned by Dr Menzies, the local G.P.

Willing hands had helped to lay out the articles, and fortunately, word of the exhibition had gone round the district, so that folk came crowding in all day, paying their fifty pence in aid of the Church Roof Repair Fund.

By late afternoon the fund had been given a real boost and the minister was beaming.

"Yours has been one of the most admired contributions," he told a couple who came in an hour before the exhibition was due to close.

The young Lauders remained looking at the bedspread after he moved away. Used to seeing it covering a modern-style bed in their new home, they decided it looked better than ever in its present surroundings.

"It's just perfect on that sort of bed," Jenny Lauder said at last. "We should get a four-poster!" she joked.

"For our wee room?" Her husband Kevin grinned. "We'd have no space left!"

"Anyway, we'll get it back tonight," Jenny remarked with satisfaction. "I wouldn't want anything to happen to it, not after all its history."

"You were working on it the first time I saw you," Kevin whispered tenderly. "Remember? You were in your gran's garden."

"I'll never forget," she assured him.

STITCHES IN TIME

BUT that meeting had happened towards the end of the long, strange history of the patchwork cover.

The beginning of it was 'way back in the dark days of 1917, when Jenny's grandmother was a slim young girl, and deeply anxious about the man she had promised to marry.

Missing in France for months, word had come at last that Corporal Thomas Fraser was a prisoner-of-war. Later still, Betsy Smith received a pencil-written letter, and though much anxiety still lay ahead, she could hope once more.

It was to her mother she spoke of the suggestion Tom had made in his brief letter.

"He says I'm not to sit worrying," the girl informed her mother. "He says I should start on some bit of work, make something for our house, and it'll help to pass the time for me."

by ANNE MURRAY

Mrs Smith nodded approvingly, remembering the times she had seen her daughter sitting listlessly, her knitting pins idle in her lap, while she worried about Tom.

Not that the girl didn't have plenty to do! She had the knitting for the troops, her days helping at the local canteen, and other days when she worked on her father's farm. But this would be different . . .

At last, Betsy hit on the plan of making a patchwork bedspread. New material was difficult to obtain these days, but this could be made out of scraps. It would be something not only for the house she hoped to share with Tom but for their bed.

Yes, that was what she would make, and Miss Pirrie at the other end of the village would show her how to do it. Miss Pirrie knew all there was in the world about sewing!

Well, it took time to learn, and was certainly not something that could be made quickly. Weeks, months even, slipped away while Betsy worked in such spare time as she had, cutting out the little six-sided bits of material, and counting the ones necessary for the pattern Miss Pirrie advised her to set in. Then sewed them together with careful stitches, aided by a small cardboard hexagonal template to keep it all straight.

Slowly, the work grew. Three hundred and ten patches were in place by the beginning of 1919 when Tom came home, a gaunt man in place of the sturdy youth who had gone away four years ago. But he was still the Tom she adored.

There was no time to do more than show him the half-made cover, then get on with the more exciting job of finding a house and arranging the wedding.

"I'll finish it after we're quite settled down," Betsy promised herself.

B UT there was so much to do looking after her little house, preparing nice meals for Tom, and going out with him of an evening, that the days simply flew by. It seemed no time until they had been married a year and then the first of their three children arrived.

There was knitting to do, as well as tapes to sew on, small socks to darn . . . there just wasn't time for the bedspread.

Carefully wrapped in a pillowslip to keep it clean, Betsy did look at it every now and then. Sometimes she showed it to her only daughter, explaining what a help it had been when she started it.

Called after herself, the girl was usually known as Bette. A lively pretty youngster, she teased her mother about never having finished the work.

"If there's another war you can get down to it again!" she said lightheartedly, never once realising that such a thing really would come.

When at last it did come, Betsy couldn't believe it. A widow now for the past two years, she prayed that it would end before her teenage sons were the age for call-up.

It was such a different sort of war, too, she felt. There was the threat of air raids even in this country area. Yet some things were as before. Once again troops came to form a big camp in the vicinity, and once again there was a canteen where she helped.

NINETEEN years old now, Bette was busy as well. Her work in the County Food Office was a reserved occupation, and she spent long hours there. She was also on duty for fire-watching at weekends and on evenings during the week.

For months there wasn't even the hint of a raid, and sitting there hour after hour became boring.

It was a sudden thought of the bedspread that prompted her to ask her mother if she could add to it.

"I'll soon find out how to do it," Bette said confidently. "There are ages when nothing happens, and you said you found it was a good thing to help the time to pass."

"So it was!" her mother agreed. "Yes, you see if you can finish it. Then you can have it as a wedding present!"

Bette laughed gaily. Prettier than ever now that she was grown-up, it was easy to see her heart wasn't involved with any of the young soldiers who came about the place.

So she set to work on the bedspread and had added over a hundred more little hexagons when the Canadians came to the camp.

Right from the moment they met, something began between her and Don Smith. Of course, the fact that his name was the same as her mother's maiden name made a link.

Don was sure that somewhere in the past they must have been related and took to calling himself her twenty-first cousin once removed.

"Just as well I'm a cousin, not a brother!" he said boldly one evening as they walked together under the stars.

"I've got two brothers, thank you, and don't need any more," Bette retorted.

"And you don't want me as one, eh? Well, I don't want you as a sister," Don declared. "But what about something else . . . "

Bette told him not to be silly. She didn't know him nearly well enough for that sort of nonsense.

STILL, deep in her heart, she felt she *did* know him well enough. As the days passed, her love for the big handsome Canadian deepened, so it was a blow when he told her they were leaving the district in another two weeks.

"Where are you going?" she asked fearfully.

He shrugged.

"They don't tell chaps like me," he replied. "I guess it'll be this Second Front you hear about. Don't look like that, love, I'll come back to you when it's all over."

The kiss they exchanged was so warm that it seemed impossible anything could go wrong between them in the few days before Don left.

Bette was never quite sure how the trouble began. She had thought she was sensible enough not to mind if she saw Don speaking to another girl, yet when she turned a corner on her way home from work one afternoon and came face to face with him and Maisie Connor walking hand in hand, she felt as if her world had crashed.

It was no good Don protesting later that he had encountered Maisie only a moment before, that she had seized his hand just as Bette came round the corner.

She couldn't see that he needed to speak to a flighty piece like Maisie at all . . . not after the things he had said to herself.

"You obviously didn't know I was going to get home early for once," she told him accusingly. "It makes me wonder how you've been spending your time lately while I've been slaving at work!"

"Say, I've been working as well," he reminded her. "I've hardly spoken twice to that kid — "

"She's no kid," Bette broke in. "Not Maisie! And you can't tell her anything about how to fascinate men."

"Listen, she doesn't fascinate me," he declared. "You've absolutely no call to be jealous."

"I'm not jealous!" Bette retorted angrily.

"Well, it looks real like you were!"

So it went on. It was Don who made an attempt to heal the breach before he went away. When he called at the house, Bette was sewing furiously at the bedspread, trying to calm her confused thoughts, yet still unable to put out of mind that glimpse of Don and Maisie together.

Don was nervous, not sure what to say.

"That's a cute bit of work," he began, picking up a corner of the spread.

It was an unfortunate start. Bette snatched the work from him and announced that she was trying to keep it clean.

"My mother began making this in the first war, and I'm finishing it in this one," she informed him, her own nervousness making her speak in much too formal a manner.

"But what is it?" he asked.

"A bedspread, of course. Look!"

She unfolded it, and saw his eyes widen.

"For covering a bed? Gee, you'll never get that done in this war. It'll take years —"

Downstream

BY shops and houses, old and new,
Beneath the city bridge it flows,
Past streets with people hurrying,
And cars and vans in moving rows.

Now, out where anchored small boats bob,
And skimming yachts have scarlet sails;
Where pleasure steamers glide upstream
With children waving by the rails!

Alongside flour mills with their wheels,
It swirls so fast across the weir,
To splash and sparkle in the sun
Where salmon leap and tumble here.

Away through meadows then it sweeps,
Where songs of skylarks echo free —
A river holds enchantment and
True beauty all its own for me.

Eileen Sweeney.

"I will so get it done!" Bette's angry reply didn't help matters any. Both of them tense and worried, the quarrel broke out again and they parted in anger.

When he left the district, Bette suffered tortures of anxiety, wondering if she would even hear if he was wounded or killed. Nor could she bear the sight of the bedspread. It was put back in the pillowslip and tucked away on a high shelf.

At Christmas-time a card came from him, addressed to Mrs and Miss Fraser, but giving no address to which a reply could be sent. It was signed rather formally: "D. Smith."

The war ended and at least he was safe. The next Christmas card came from Canada, again with no address. Year after year it continued, and year after year Bette thought unhappily of her own part in that stupid quarrel. She couldn't understand now how she had been so foolish.

And she still loved him.

What on earth was the use of that, she would wonder sadly.

I T was in 1957 that something happened at last to break the routine in which she now lived, working away as usual and still staying with her mother. One Saturday afternoon a large car arrived in the village and made its way to the Frasers' home.

Bette saw it from the window as she sat there, getting the best of the light for what she was doing.

Afterwards she was to think what an extraordinary thing it was that only that day had she taken out the bedspread and decided to begin work on it again.

"Is that a car stopping?" asked Mrs Fraser as she woke from an afternoon nap.

"A huge car!" Bette replied. "There's a man getting out. Oh!"

Her cry brought Mrs Fraser out of her chair. She too looked through the window.

She too recognised the man for whom her daughter had yearned so long.

Mrs Fraser had liked Don Smith. She had felt he would make Bette a good husband and to see the girl's face now revealed much.

Beaming, she hurried to open the door.

"Why, Don, come away in! It's grand to see you again," she told him warmly.

Bette said nothing. She sat there, with the bedspread falling about her feet, and her blue eyes were like stars.

To Don, she didn't seem a day older, and her smile gave him the welcome he wanted.

Yet there was a sense of embarrassment about their meeting. Only that could have made him begin with such a tactless remark.

"What? Still at that thing?" he exclaimed. "I thought you were going to finish it during the war!"

Bette grew pink. How could she tell him she hadn't the heart to work on it after he left? But she made an effort.

"Oh, I forgot all about it for ages," she said, smiling carelessly. Don had booked into the hotel just outside the town. He had so much to tell them. It seemed he had done very well in business in Montreal after his demobilisation. He had often longed to return and try to make things up, but instead, he had waited until he could safely leave his affairs in other hands for a time.

H E had always meant to come to Scotland again, though scarcely daring to hope Bette would still be free.

As for himself, when they walked once more under the stars that evening, arm in arm, he told her that in all those years he had never seen another girl he wanted.

A day or two after that he asked her to marry him. The thought of a home so far away held no fears for Bette , and she knew she could leave her mother with an easy mind since her two brothers were now married and lived close at hand.

"I'll be fine," Mrs Fraser assured her. "Some day maybe I'll come and visit you."

"I'm counting on that," Bette told her.

There was just one problem.

Don had to return to Canada in another four weeks at the most and he wanted the wedding to take place before then. It would be so wonderful to have Bette with him when he returned.

But Bette hesitated. They spent a whole morning discussing it, then she promised to give him a final decision that evening.

"I really will try to make plans," she said earnestly.

When he arrived, once more she was at work on the bedspread and Mrs Fraser was away out to the Guild meeting. Don felt sure he could coax her round to his way of thinking in the time they would be alone.

"Well, darling, have you settled it all?" he asked her. "Oh, Bette, you will marry me before I go back, won't you?"

The urgency in his voice flustered Bette. She was ready to do what he wanted, but for a moment she continued sewing, with her head bent over the work.

"I wish you'd put that old thing down, Bette!" exclaimed Don. "You don't need to keep on at it. Anyway, I guess by now you could do it with your eyes closed. It can't be difficult."

Bette dropped her needle and looked at him.

"Oh, can't it?" she cried. "That's just the way a man would talk. And what man could put in the work my mother and I have done — "

"I could!" he broke in somewhat rashly. "I've never met any job yet that has beaten me, and I'm a dab hand at sewing on buttons."

"Buttons!" Bette said scornfully. "That's not in the same street as this.

"All right, if you're so sure about your skill, just take the bedspread and see if you can add a bit. In fact, if you set in fifty more bits and keep to my pattern I'll . . . I'll marry you as soon as you wish."

Don eyed her uneasily. He gathered up the material she tossed at him and stood with it in his arms looking helpless.

Had he really to do this impossible thing to gain the reward he so much desired?

However, he hadn't got where he was by backing away from a challenge. Right! If a woman could do this sort of work, so could he!

"You'd better give me some of these pieces you've cut out already," he suggested coolly.

Bette was beginning to regret her hasty words. Whatever happened, she was going to marry him. But she began to count through the small bits of material.

"There's forty-three here," she told him. "That'll do. I'll put them into this box, and there are some needles and thread. And some of the cardboard patterns. You need them to keep it all even."

Gosh, she really did mean him to do it, thought Don. But he took the box she held out and said goodnight rather stiffly.

ONCE back in his hotel bedroom he gave a rueful glance into the mirror.

"You big fool!" he told himself.

It took him till midnight to work out how to attach a hexagon neatly. It was four o'clock next morning when he had three more on.

"Thirty-nine still to do!" he groaned as he got wearily into bed. "Oh, well, it may get easier as I go on."

Several days passed before he again called at the Frasers' house and Bette's heart thumped uncomfortably as she went to let him in.

It was just as well, she thought, that her mother was out seeing a neighbour, for Mrs Fraser had been very puzzled by the sudden disappearance of the young man.

Now perhaps they could get everything cleared up satisfactorily before she returned . . .

Don was carrying the familiar pillowslip. He took out the bedspread and unfolded it in silence.

"You . . . you've done it!" Bette gasped. "I never dreamed you would manage."

With the bedspread once more crumpled on the floor between them, they exchanged kisses which cleared the air completely and a date for the wedding was settled before Mrs Fraser came in.

"But don't ever ask me to hold a needle again," Don requested Bette when he was saying goodnight to her much later on. "You bad girl, setting me a task like that! I've sat up half of each night and hardly gone out all day doing the wretched thing!"

"Oh, Don, dearest Don, I'm sorry! I spoke without thinking," she confessed. "You must cure me of that."

After the ups and downs of the courtship, the marriage turned out very well and Bette was happy in Canada.

But she didn't take the bedspread with her. She felt it would always remind her how unkind she had been to Don.

So once more it was put away on the high shelf. Occasionally, Mrs Fraser wondered if she should try to finish it, but before she got down to it she had something much more interesting to do.

Word came from Canada that Bette was expecting a baby, so again, that meant knitting little woollies, then crocheting a big fleecy shawl, and then in a great hurry making a second shawl.

FOR it was twins that arrived — a boy and girl. Accounts of their progress came regularly from Canada, along with requests for more knitting. It might have been thought that the bedspread was quite forgotten.

Not so! It became the centre of a story Don liked to tell his children when they were old enough, and of course it lost nothing in the telling!

"Your mother nearly didn't marry me," he would say gravely to young Tom and Jenny. "She threw a great big bedcover at me and said I had to finish making it, and if I did she would marry me."

"And you sat up nights and never went to bed," little Jenny would put in.

"And you sewed so hard all day that you got a hole in your finger," Tom added sympathetically.

It was when the twins were ten that Grannie Fraser came to visit, and it was from her Jenny learnt that the bedspread hadn't been finished after all.

"I should have brought it out with me," Mrs Fraser said regretfully. "You might have finished it when you were older, Jenny."

Again the years passed, and in due course Jenny was twenty. Her twin was now hard at work in the family business, but she wanted to travel.

And where else should she start but with Scotland, where her grandmother still lived, remarkably active for a woman of eighty.

So Jenny flew over, and loved every bit of Scotland that she saw, and also got on splendidly with her grandmother.

GUESS what, Gran," Jenny said one day. "I'm going to finish that bedspread for you.

"I've heard such stories about it from Dad that I'm not going home till I can tell him I've done it. He's so proud of having found out all by himself how to do it!"

"Aye, and he made a good job of it too," Mrs Fraser said. "I couldn't think where he had got to that week, never coming near us," she reminisced.

It seemed Jenny had done patchwork before. She had made a little cover for a baby's cot while at school.

Looking at the cover, she could see a good many more patches were still needed.

Then get on with at once, she told herself. It was such a fine afternoon that when Gran had her nap she sat in the pleasant little summer house at the foot of the garden. Only a few garden tools were there, and she spread a newspaper to make sure of keeping her work clean.

It was quiet and peaceful sitting there working away, but all at once Jenny heard the click of the front gate. She could see a young man entering, but he didn't go to the door. Goodness, he was going inside!

Jenny jumped to her feet, her heart fluttering, but ready to rush forward and deal with this intruder. Before she could disentangle herself from the folds of the bedspread he had emerged and now was heading straight for the summer house. She grew pale.

BUT her presence seemed to startle the young man as much as his alarmed her. There was a pause while they regarded each other, then suddenly he smiled.

"You must be Mrs Fraser's granddaughter," he said. "I heard you had come across from Canada. Did you wonder why I walked in at the back door? It was to get the key for this place so that I could take out the hoe. Your gran lets me come to do her garden when I'm free.

"My name's Kevin Lauder," he told her. "I know yours is Jenny."

Another smile was exchanged. Then she became aware of the entangling folds of the bedspread and began to gather it up. It was easy to explain its history to this new friend.

"My dad never tires of boasting about his share in it." She laughed.

"He must be pretty smart," Kevin said admiringly. "I can't see myself ever knowing how to do it. I can't even sew on a button, but then my mother does all that sort of thing for me. She's always on at me to find myself a wife!" he added with a pretended groan.

"And haven't you found one yet?" Jenny asked impishly.

"No . . . at least, I'm not so sure . . . now," he said boldly.

So now Jenny is Mrs Kevin Lauder, happily settled in her Scottish home. Her parents have been over on a visit, and it need hardly be said that Don wanted to point out to everyone the exact part of the bedspread which he had completed!

At last, it is being used as it was meant to be used. If it is by a member of the third generation what does that matter?

It is still a magnificent piece of work which will very definitely be treasured as the family heirloom which it has certainly become. □

One Day

by CLAIRE DEMAINE

In Spring

THE warm spring sunshine seemed to beckon to Grace through the kitchen window, but resolutely she turned her back on it.

It's such a lovely day, she thought. Just perfect for taking a walk through the woods to the cottage, her treacherous senses told her. The breeze gently opened the door a little way and Grace sniffed appreciatively as the delicious scent drifted into the kitchen.

She was reminded instantly of the dell just short of the cottage — that's how the air always seemed to smell near her mother's house . . .

Not like here, she thought rebelliously, when the breeze lifted the curtains beside her and reminded her what a lovely drying day it would be. She hurried off to fetch the covers from the bedrooms upstairs.

It was pointless to even consider going to her old home.

There might not be as good a day for drying a big wash for weeks, especially not on her day off work.

Grace sighed as she stripped the covers from the beds, thinking that going back to work had been welcome and exciting, when it had only been part-time. It had seemed like a heaven-sent opportunity to get away from the everlasting round of washing and cleaning.

She had soon found that there were ways of cutting down on the housework. It wasn't really all that important to clean the windows every Friday, or polish the bedroom furniture as often as that downstairs.

In fact, Grace even began to wonder why she'd been making such a slave of herself all the years the girls had been growing up. Of course when they were tiny there had been more to do, but once they had started school the house had been less untidy.

At least it had been until recently, Grace thought wryly, as she gazed round the chaos in the girls' bedroom.

Automatically she began to pick up tights which had been flung over the chair, records which were propped on the edge of the dressing-table, and magazines from under the beds. All at once she realised what she was doing.

This was the girls' room, she reminded herself. They were supposed to keep it tidy and clean, so what on earth was she doing clearing up after them! That had been part of the bargain when Grace had taken a full-time job . . .

"We'll help, Mum." Carol was fourteen now and full of good intentions. "I mean, more than we do now," she had added hastily as she caught her mother's sceptical glance. "Not just with the washing-up and things, but *really* help."

"Of course we will!" At sixteen, Shirley had, for once, been in agreement with Carol. "It's time you got out and about a bit, Mum. Make a career for yourself before it's too late," she had added, with youthful candour. "There's loads of things we could do to help since we'll be home before you anyway."

S O Grace had taken a job at the local garden centre and now revelled at being in touch with the country again even in this small way.

When she and Eric were married Grace had missed the garden round the cottage, and the nearness of the woods and fields. But Eric worked in the city and though the house they had bought had been on the outskirts, the area had become more and more built-up over the years. Eric maintained that their small plot of ground was quite enough for him to keep tidy, so Grace found herself satisfying her love of nature in her work at the garden centre.

But it was on mornings like this one, when the sun was shining and a breeze was bringing the scents of the countryside to her, that her thoughts turned first to her childhood home, then reluctantly to the prospect of a line full of freshly-washed bedding.

With the covers bundled into her arms, Grace turned from her bedroom window and looked out over the rooftops to where she could almost imagine the real countryside began.

I suppose I could just put these into the machine and go, she thought. But as she turned, her eyes fell on the suit hanging on the wardrobe door. Her spirits sank abruptly.

Eric had hung his suit there to remind her.

As they'd been preparing for bed the night before, he'd asked Grace what she had planned for the next day.

"If you're going into town, of course," he had added, having asked her to take his suit to the cleaners. "I suppose I could drop it in sometime this week if you're not."

He had waited hopefully for her assent, and when none came his voice had taken on a martyred tone. "But I do need it for the meeting on Friday and it means cutting my lunch hour drastically if I take it myself."

Grace had felt like asking him how he thought she was going to do the errand if not by cutting into her precious spare time, but she had held the words in check.

She had just come back into the bedroom after having a shower and, as she felt the heat of the bedroom which caught the late afternoon sun, her thoughts had turned to the cottage where her mother lived.

I'll go over tomorrow, Grace had resolved, and then Eric had chosen that exact moment to ask her to go in exactly the opposite direction!

She hadn't dared open her mouth as frustration boiled up in her. As the silence lengthened, Eric had heaved a sigh of resignation.

"Oh, well . . ." he began.

"Of course I'll take it," she had finally ground out the words.

This morning the sight of the suit hanging there so limply seemed to mock her. She snatched it up, hearing the hanger clatter to the floor, but ignoring it, strode from the room.

What was the use of my dreaming of relaxing in a deck-chair, talking to Mum, with a glass of her lemonade in my hand, Grace asked herself furiously, stuffing the covers into the washing-machine.

Turning to the washing-basket she began to sort out the rest of the laundry and the first things she touched were a couple of jumpers and a pleated skirt of Shirley's, all of which certainly needed washing by hand.

"Those girls!" she exclaimed, uttering the words aloud. "They promised — they actually *promised* they wouldn't put other things in if they were for hand washing only."

Grace gazed indignantly at the garments and remembered the discussion there'd been over this very question when both girls had promised to do their own hand washing.

"Of course we will," Shirley had declared. "You're quite right."

"Sorry, Mum." Carol had hugged Grace. "We forget . . . But you needn't have washed that jumper, I don't like it much anyway."

This thoughtless remark had taken her mother's breath away. She had gazed after the girls, and shaken her head slowly, despairingly.

WITH an angry flick of her wrist Grace switched on the machine and ran water into the sink — perhaps if she hurried she wouldn't miss too much of the day. But as her gaze fell on the breakfast dishes stacked on the tray where Carol had left them, she slowly and deliberately turned off the rushing tap.

I won't do it, she decided. They knew I'd planned to go out today — they knew it! And Carol said she'd wash these.

Grace stared at the dirty dishes, recalling how her younger daughter had pushed at her playfully.

"You go and get all prettied up, Mum, I'll do these." Carol had grinned. "Go on!"

Grace had laughingly obeyed the order and gone upstairs. She'd taken her new spring suit from the wardrobe with a thrill of anticipation, but as she'd hunted for a clean pair of tights she'd heard the doorbell ring. Then Carol's voice had called upstairs from the hall.

"Jane's here, Mum!" she'd shouted. "I'm off!"

Grace had smilingly watched her go down the path with her friend, but when she had come down into the kitchen the sight of the unwashed dishes had told her that Jane's arrival had put paid to her daughter's good intention.

Slowly she had walked back upstairs to take off the suit and climb back into her slacks and T-shirt. There was nothing else for it, she thought with a sigh of resignation.

THE washing-machine gave a gurgle as if in agreement and Grace smiled ruefully as she surveyed the clothes and dishes waiting for her attention. Action was certainly called for and she finally made up her mind.

With a feeling of satisfaction she pulled the plug from the sink and watched the water drain away — even the sight of the wasted soap flakes didn't cause her any remorse.

"I don't care, it'll serve them right if I'm not here, waiting for them with a good meal and nicely-laundered clothes. I planned to have the whole day to myself — and I'm going to!" she exclaimed.

She felt a tingling sensation she recalled from childhood, a sensation which grew within her as she turned away from the dirty dishes. It was very definitely one of rebellion.

With feet suddenly as fleet as a girl's, Grace ran back upstairs and changed once more into her new green suit. She laughed as she brushed her hair and added a touch of lipstick. Her eyes were bright with expectation and needed no make-up to enhance their sparkle and her cheeks were flushed delicately.

She smiled approvingly to her reflection in the mirror, telling herself that she didn't look at all bad for an old married woman . . .

Closing the door firmly behind her, Grace breathed deeply of the invigorating air, feeling as if she had escaped from some prison. She laughed mischievously as she began to walk in the opposite direction from the main road and the town centre.

Grace had no regrets about leaving the girls' work undone. After all, they had all week to prepare their clothes for any weekend outings. As for Eric's suit, she had decided she could go out a little earlier next morning and leave it at the dry cleaners' on her way to work.

She didn't start at the garden centre until nine-thirty, the shop would be open by then. Eric would have his suit in time for the meeting, she assured herself. There was no reason why he should suffer from her revolt, but those girls . . .

THE road began to climb quite steeply, and Grace's steps slowed. She had left the housing estate behind her now and the road had become a lane bordered with trees. Here and there a large house peeped from between the trees, but soon even these had been replaced by the occasional farmhouse set back amongst the fields.

Steadily she climbed, leaving the lane now for a path which wove its way towards the woods she had visualised so clearly this morning. Although she could have taken the easier path and skirted May Hill, she had felt the need to pit herself against the terrain.

Even when her leg muscles began to ache and her breathing became more laboured, Grace experienced a peculiar satisfaction in the awareness that she was in control of her body. She felt alive and fit.

When she breasted the last rise Grace stood quite still for a few moments, regaining her breath and looking down into the valley.

It must be almost three years since I came this way, she mused, her eyes tracing the distant road which she normally drove along beside Eric. In the distance she picked out the red tiles of the roof of the cottage where her mother lived. It seemed to be farther away than she recalled — she'd better hurry.

Her feet found the zig-zag path which was now far more overgrown than it had been the last time. Did no-one walk this way now, she wondered. Perhaps everyone preferred to travel by car . . .

But I know how wonderful it is to walk, she thought, and that spirit of adventure bubbled to the surface again, making her reckless. Instead of placing her feet carefully, as behoved a woman with two almost grown-up daughters, Grace sprang lightly from one bend of the path to the next, quickening her pace the nearer she got to the valley bottom.

Later she was to declare that her feet must have been bewitched, or else the slope had grown much steeper. Women of her age might run after a bus but they didn't scamper down a rough hillside.

Soon her feet were lifting and striding, jumping and twisting, flying it seemed, towards the house where she had lived until she was married.

Perhaps it was the breeze holding her skirt closely about her legs, maybe it was the state of the path — or was she just too old to indulge in girlish escapades such as running down steep hillsides?

Whatever the reason, suddenly the ground was rushing up towards her as she lost her balance and her arms flailed wildly as she fell.

Grace hit the ground with an impact which robbed her of her breath and drove every thought of other injury from her mind. She lay curled in a tight ball as she gasped for breath, the blood pounding in her head so that her eyes swam with a misty redness. She felt dreadful.

DEVOTION

*I*S *this your master; you his slave?*
 You answer all his needs – he expects you so to do. His meals must be upon the dot – complains if they are not. He never washes dishes; avoids all household chores.

 There's people coming in tonight, and you so much to do; he calmly settles for a nap; never lends a helping hand. He takes all things for granted; never says a simple "thank you." Brings you no flowers, nor breakfast in your bed. Yet you love him – love him!

 For he can only give what's only in his power to give: his full unfaltering devotion, he is your dog!

Rev. T. R. S. Campbell.

When at last her lungs stopped their agonised heaving, she lay still, waiting for the world to settle around her. She lay for aching, fear-filled moments before she dared try to sit up and assess the damage. Then fear welled up in her again as she looked at her strangely-twisted ankle, and felt the pain begin to throb up her leg.

Using the branch of a tree, Grace pulled herself to her feet, but as she tested her weight gingerly upon the injured ankle, one fleeting thought flashed through her mind before she crumpled into a heap again — *now they'll know just how much I do*. Then she lost consciousness.

The sun had risen high in the sky by the time she came round, but Grace discovered that despite its rays, she was shivering. Clearly she couldn't stay here.

With an effort she managed to sit up, leaning back against the tree, but her strength was spent with the effort. As she gazed around her she saw that it wasn't only the pain which was making her senses swim. She was half-lying downhill.

Carefully she edged her body round, lifting her foot with her hands clasped round her calf after each gradual move. When at last she was facing the right way she heaved a heartfelt sigh of relief.

Not only did she feel better, but she saw that she was now at the bottom of the hill. There, a few hundred yards away, stood the gate of her old home.

The task of turning her body round had brought her out in a sweat but, even so, it was more comfortable than the shivers she'd been experiencing before.

WELL, it's no use shouting," she decided, speaking aloud. "Mum will probably be getting her lunch, even supposing I was near enough." The sound of her even voice was comforting and she continued. "Somehow I've got to get to her . . . I wonder if my ankle's broken or simply sprained."

There was no need to panic, she told herself. Of course not!

Across the field, not that very far away, her mother was probably standing in her kitchen preparing her lunch — what could be more normal than that? All she had to do was to crawl a yard or two, or three, or . . .

Tears sprang to her eyes as Grace thought of her mother. She knew she'd be in for a telling-off when she finally made it to the cottage.

She fancied she could hear her mother's voice issuing intructions. *Don't just sit there, you silly girl,* it seemed to say. *Hitch yourself along.*

So taking her weight on her hands, Grace moved a little way across the grass. *Don't go too fast,* the voice seemed to tell her, as once more sweat broke out on her forehead. She began to move again but a little slower this time.

It took a long, long time, but eventually Grace was resting against the garden gate, looking sorrowfully down at the grassy stains on her skirt.

I hope it will clean, she thought, then stifled a desire to giggle. If only she'd gone to the dry-cleaners' that morning all this wouldn't have happened.

Still, maybe they've got one of those offers on — two articles for the price of one. She chuckled. Surely I deserve something to make up for this.

MRS McBRIDE was a sensible person and wasted no breath on recriminations, when Grace finally managed to attract her attention. With one anxious and alarmed cry, she dropped the towel she was holding and rushed to put an arm round her daughter's shoulders to help her into the cottage. After settling her comfortably on the sofa she telephoned their doctor.

When he arrived later he shook his head at Grace when she told him what had happened.

"You always were a harum-scarum child," he chided gently, "but I thought you were supposed to be grown up now. Haven't you two girls of your own?"

With a blush, Grace admitted that she had. How could she possibly describe to this elderly man the feeling of freedom she'd experienced when she'd abandoned her household tasks — of the exhilaration of flying down that hillside?

"I slipped," she said simply. "And the path's not as good as it used to be . . ."

"And the policemen are all wee boys these days, and the newspapers are using smaller type." The doctor smiled. "I know the feeling quite well!"

Grace gave up. It was useless to protest that she wasn't that old — she wasn't that young either.

"I suppose that family of yours can look after themselves?" he said, preparing to leave.

Mrs McBride answered for her.

"Of course they can. Grace has brought them up to be self-reliant, though how I can't imagine. I certainly waited on *her* hand and foot," she added, smiling affectionately to her daughter.

Grace stared in surprise at her mother's retreating back as she showed the doctor out. What on earth did she mean?

Hadn't she always had to keep her own room clean? Do her own washing? Mend her stockings? Shop for her own toothpaste? In fact, all the things she tried to instil into Carol and Shirley?

SHE had to admit it was nice to be mollycoddled now, though. Grace snuggled down, recalling the other times she had lain on this same sofa being looked after just like Mum was doing today — it was like being a child all over again.

I suppose Mum was right, just a little, she thought drowsily. I did get round her. Yes, I suppose I was spoiled . . .

Just as her eyes were growing heavy, Grace heard her mother's quiet steps returning.

"Can I get you anything, dear?" Mrs McBride asked, as mothers have always asked.

"That's what mothers are for," she whispered to her bewildered mother. But Mrs McBride wasn't to hear any more because Grace was on the brink of sleep and the words became unexpressed thoughts.

That's what mothers are for — for loving. I suppose it works all ways, doesn't it, Mum, she thought dreamily. The girls have me and I have you. I love them and I love you and . . .

But Mrs McBride couldn't have heard any more, even if Grace had stayed awake long enough to finish the thought, because she had already left the room to go to phone Eric.

"It'll be nice having her to coddle for a day or so," she murmured, as she lifted the receiver. □

By
MARIAN
FARQUHARSON

Season Fo

I T was still snowing hard: thick cotton-wool flakes whirling madly in all directions. A waist-high drift barricaded the garage doors, but, thankfully, I wouldn't be needing my car tonight.

With a swift tug at the heavy, velvet curtains, I blotted out King Winter's cheerless landscape, and took up a slipper-toasting position at the fireside. The cat half opened a solemn yellow eye, forbidding me to oust her from the cosiest chair. Then, seeing that all was well, she resumed her mouse-filled dreams.

The old clock on the mantel ticked companionably and I settled down to enjoy a snug and cosy Christmas Eve. Later, I'd have to don Eskimo layers of clothing before venturing forth to the nearby kirk for the candle-lit Midnight Service — but that was hours ahead. I mustn't fall asleep . . .

The phone rang. It was my married sister, who lived some ten miles distant, worrying about snow-blocked roads and my Christmas Day visit.

"They say the ploughs can't get through," Mary fretted. "The snow's drifting to the height of a man. I'd hate to think of you marooned in the glen, whilst we're all tucking into roast turkey and plum pudding."

"The weather should ease a bit by morning," I said confidently, suppressing my doubts. "Anyway, I've got snow-chains fitted on the car."

"Well, don't you be taking any risks now, however much we hope to see you." The whooping of excited children drowned her voice. "It's a mad house here," she shouted gaily over the din. "If Santa's sleigh gets lost in the snow, the noise will lead him straight to us!"

Smiling, I replaced the receiver, Mary's small house was packed tight as a sardine can at Christmas-time, with her children and young grandchildren all coming to stay. I would certainly miss the warmth of a lively family gathering, if I were unable to make the trip tomorrow.

I didn't expect any more calls tonight. As a community midwife who was retiring in the New Year, the "hot" line to my cottage had already cooled. Someone else would welcome the glen's next crop of babies into this world, leaving me with plenty of time on my hands. I was certainly going to miss my busy, rewarding life.

But before I'd tackled a row of knitting, there came an urgent knocking at the door. Surely Mrs MacDuff over at Langbrae hadn't decided to bring forward her fifth happy event, expressly to keep me on my toes to the bitter end?

Rejoicing

I undid the latch and, to my relief, it wasn't hearty Farmer MacDuff who stood there like a walking snowman, with the blizzard raging round him. My heart warmed to see Rory Colquhoun.

"You've picked a shocking night to call." I laughed. "Come away in and I'll make you a good, warm drink . . ." Of all my "babies" I'd always had a soft spot for young Rory. There was a long-standing feud between him and his father, old Colonel Colquhoun, but it was none of my business.

Carol

CLEAR upon the midnight air,
    Sound of angel voices rare.
Brightly gleams the guiding Star,
Leading shepherds from afar.

Three wise men came, their gifts to bear,
To the Christ-child lying there.
Saw His Mother, meek and lowly,
With the Infant, pure and holy.

The Heavenly Babe, sent from above,
A messenger of Peace and Love.
The merry bells shall sweetly ring,
With children's voices carolling.
Dorothy M. Loughran

"Shift the cat from that chair and you can tell me all your news. It's almost two years since I last clapped eyes on you . . ."

"I'm afraid I'm not on a social call, Miss Burns," he gasped. "I need you professionally — and please hurry! My wife's in labour, five weeks early!"

I bit back a host of questions, for this was no time for gossiping. Presumably the Colonel had at last welcomed his "black sheep" son back into the fold.

Rory had incurred his father's lasting displeasure by leaving agricultural college in order to drift around the world, long haired and bearded, painting pictures for his daily bread. And the lad had lingered long enough in the East to find himself an almond-eyed bride.

"Calm yourself," I said briskly. "First babies usually take their time over entering the world. I'll just have a word with Dr Robertson on the phone, then we'll be straight round to Loch House and your wife."

He gave a deep sigh. "We're not staying with my father. He doesn't even know we're here. Do you know Brechin Croft, 'way above Rob MacDuff's steading?"

I had to think a moment. "You *can't* mean the old cottage owned by that actor fellow from London, that chap who's only here once in a blue moon? Why, Rory, it's practically tumbling down!"

"Any port in a storm," he said quietly. "We've been living in a basement studio in London, and our landlord finally gave us notice to quit. Not that I blame him, you understand. He didn't particularly fancy an armful of paintings in lieu of rent!"

Homeless and desperately hard-up, Rory had had a sudden inspiration. The happy-go-lucky owner of Brechin Croft, with whom he used to fish the Colonel's loch in summers past, had virtually given him the freedom of his remote holiday hideaway.

"Danny's somewhere in Australia, touring with an acting company," Rory explained, "but I'll square things with him when he returns."

Loading their few earthly possessions into an ancient van fit for the scrap heap, the young couple had headed for the glen where, hopefully, Rory might find employment of some kind.

I dialled Dr Robertson's number, only to learn from his wife that he was stranded overnight at the Cottage Hospital, as the roads were impassable.

Muffled to the eyebrows, I loaded my equipment on to a sled, and lifted the big storm lantern from its hook. "I hope you've a good fire burning, we'll need gallons of hot water," I said cheerily.

Rory and I stepped out into the night, leaving the cat in sole possession of the glowing fire, well protected by a safety guard.

IT was a nightmare trek, and soon I lost all sense of time and place. On and steadily upwards we trudged, stumbling blindly, with Rory's stout stick testing the shifting depths of snow.

The lights of the MacDuffs' homestead flickered dimly ahead, like a mirage in the swirling wastes. "You could have used their telephone," I said pointedly, as we paused to get our breath back.

"And leave you to brave the elements alone?" he retorted with a grin. "Midwives aren't too plentiful round about here, so I couldn't risk losing one in a ten-foot drift!"

As the summer retreat of a carefree bachelor, Brechin Croft left much to be desired in the way of amenities, but in mid-winter it was grim indeed.

Arctic blasts rattled ill-fitting window frames and Rory's incompetent tinkering with the wood-burning stove had produced little but acrid clouds of smoke. If only I could have transported my blazing fire along with me!

Huddled in a tatty blanket, the girl from the faraway land smiled shyly. She was a fairy-like creature, with porcelain skin and jet-black hair which shimmered in the lamp-light.

"This is Pearl, my wife," Rory said proudly, and the girl extended a welcoming hand.

"I'm so happy you're here, Miss Burns." Her voice sounded like a tinkling silver bell. "Forgive me for dragging you from your fireside."

"Oh, bairns can't always arrive on a summer's day," I replied lightly, donning a starched white apron. "Now, let's make you more comfortable, my dear . . ."

Rory was hovering helplessly and I promptly ordered him to fetch more kindling from the woodstore. Expectant fathers are best kept fully employed, and this young man would find himself tackling many a chore before the night was through!

Pearl's bonnie face clouded as a sudden spasm gripped her. Tightly, she clung to my hand.

"There, there," I soothed, "just try to relax now. Everything's going to be all right."

But already I was concerned, for the birth wasn't going to be plain sailing, and in these primitive conditions I dreaded any serious complications. How could I summon help?

Very gently, I broke the news she was having twins.

The long night dragged on and there were moments of great anxiety. I wished it were possible to transfer my patient to the maternity wing of the Cottage Hospital with its splendid modern equipment, but no ambulance could fight its way through the Arctic conditions.

The lives of Rory's wife and his unborn bairns were my responsibility alone and it was weighing heavily.

But then, deeply troubled by Pearl's increasing weakness, I suddenly remembered that this was Christmas Night! Two thousand years ago, the Holy Infant had been born, not in luxurious surroundings but in an ox's stall. Had winter winds howled cruelly then, with snow lying deep outside?

Time had added a golden lustre to that humble stable scene, but all at once I became fully aware of the incredible wonder of the Nativity: not just seeing it as a beautiful picture on a Christmas card, but as a real-life happening — when *the Word became flesh and dwelt among us.*

S ILENTLY I began to pray and, slowly, a wonderful calm seemed to permeate that squalid, cheerless little room. I began to hum a carol very softly, aware that I no longer worked alone, for there are times when we are given strength and skill far beyond our own.

Towards dawn, as the darkness imperceptibly faded from the sky, Alexander Rory and David Bruce Colquhoun arrived safely.

Pearl was sitting up, exhausted but triumphant, sipping tea. "So very tiny," she murmured, glancing at her sons, who shared the carrycot gladly loaned by Mrs MacDuff.

"Babies always look like skinned rabbits!" Rory commented, but the pride in his eyes spoke volumes.

Towards midday, after a harrowing journey from the hospital, Dr Robertson arrived on Farmer MacDuff's tractor. It had now stopped snowing.

Anxiously I awaited the elderly doctor's verdict. "You've not done too badly all on your own, my girl," he proclaimed, during our little medical chinwag, and from him that was praise indeed! "The bairns are light-weights, certainly, but there's no immediate cause for alarm . . ."

Just to be on the safe side, he proposed moving mother and babies to the maternity unit, where expert staff could keep a constant watch.

"It'll be a dicey journey for the ambulance," he prophesied grimly, "but the police will get it through safely."

And so they did — aided by a snowplough and a score of willing diggers! A couple of hours later I was dropped at my cottage door, whilst the ambulance bearing its precious cargo headed for the Cottage Hospital, flanked by a police escort.

Rory had insisted on accompanying his family, though to my mind he'd give the nurses more bother than his tiny sons!

I had already phoned my sister Mary from the MacDuffs', explaining I'd be unable to attend the family party.

"Trust you to be on duty to the bitter end!" She laughed. "Well, we'll save some cold turkey for a sandwich, love."

So now there was nothing left to do but let the cat out and soak myself in a good, hot bath, before clambering thankfully into bed. It had been a very long night.

But then I thought of Loch House and a lonely, embittered old man who had just become a grandfather twice over and didn't know it.

When I'd ventured to suggest to Rory that a message be sent to the Colonel, he'd shrugged, mumbling vaguely about news travelling fast enough on the local grapevine!

"I'll not go begging to my father for help," he muttered darkly, "not after all the hurtful things he said to me!" Rory could be obstinate, too.

Strictly speaking, it was not my concern, but I've never feared interfering in other folk's affairs for their own good, and it was high time the old warrior laid aside his battle weapons . . .

IT was in a distinctly militant frame of mind that I jangled the iron doorbell of Loch House. Mrs Fordyce, the housekeeper, who'd grown brusque and surly like her widowed employer, extended a poor welcome.

"We weren't expecting anyone on Christmas Day," she said bluntly, "but I'll see if the Colonel can spare a moment."

After a lengthy wait in the draughty, panelled hall, I was shown into his cosy study. The Colonel laid a book aside with ill-concealed reluctance. "And how are you keeping, Miss Burns?" he enquired with a thin smile. "It's a rare event for anyone to call by nowadays . . ."

"I'm not here for a social chat," I assured him. "I've come to bring news of a happy event! Your son's wife gave birth to twins early today; you've two fine wee grandsons, Colonel Colquhoun!"

Expressionless he listened to my news, with only the rapid drumming of his fingers on the chair arm betraying his inner emotion.

At last he spoke: "I appreciate your troubling to come here, but you should have spared yourself the walk! What Rory does with his life is his own affair. I want no part in it." He gave a bitter laugh. "I never thought I'd see the day when the family would sink to this!

"There's been Colquhouns here at Loch House these past three hundred years, every one with good Scots blood in their veins — not a foreigner amongst them. My poor, dear wife must be turning in her grave!"

"Maybe so," I snapped, "but only because she's ashamed to hear you speak like that about your own son and grandsons! What harm have these two innocent wee bairns done to you?" Properly steamed up now, I said a great deal more which is best forgotten.

Towering with rage, he rose to his feet. "I'll not insult a visitor under my roof — but the sooner you leave the better!"

"And gladly!" I hit back, making for the door. "I'll not bandy words with a man who has a heart of stone!"

I closed the study door firmly behind me. "I'll see myself out," I shouted, asking myself why on earth I'd come on this hopeless task.

THE phone was shrilling the moment I set foot in my cottage. Upset and shaky, I answered it.

"Miss Burns?" The Colonel's strident tones came barking down the line.

"Look," I began in order to forestall further unpleasantness on Christmas Day, "I'm really sorry for my outburst just now. I'm afraid there are times when I simply speak my mind and . . ."

"Be quiet, woman!" he said tersely. "Will you let a man get a word in edgeways? I just want you to know that I'm on my way to the Cottage Hospital — and don't start giving me a lecture about driving carefully!

"I'm going to see my son and his family, in the hope that we can sort out some kind of future together. Loch House has been empty for far too long . . ."

My heart was too full to speak.

"Are you still there?" he barked.

"Yes, Colonel, and I'm delighted you've decided to make the journey."

"It's a very long journey," he went on quietly, "and I'm not just speaking about icy roads. Rory and I have drifted thousands of miles apart, perhaps too far ever to reach each other again."

I reminded him of the old Eastern proverb: *"The longest part of a journey is the very first step.* . . and from what I know of Rory he'll be more than willing to meet you halfway."

Deep inside me, I felt certain all would be well at Loch House, for I had sensed that Rory's days of wandering were done. With a wife and family to support, it was time for him to come to terms with life and settle down.

The Colquhouns had farmed their land well for generations and no-one could stop a farmer taking up a paintbrush in his spare time!

And, who could tell, maybe young Mrs Rory would be glad of a helping hand with her bairns now and again? I'd be only too happy to offer a few words of advice.

Already the winter sky was darkening fast, and, high above the glen, the first star appeared. I watched it, shining brightly, just as a long-ago star had cast its radiance over a humble stable in Bethlehem to light the paths of all mankind. □

York Minster, or the Cathedral Church of St Peter, its official name, is the largest of English mediaeval cathedrals. Here we have one of the best views of this magnificent edifice, which includes part of the city walls, dating mainly from the reign of Edward III (1327-1377). The Minster lies in the north corner of this fascinating old city, and there has been a church on this site since the seventh century.

YORK : J CAMPBELL KERR

A Question Of Some Importance

By
Peggy
Maitland

W HAT a change from yesterday," Clare Lindsay said, glancing out at the dreary Monday-morning rain. She picked up her cracker and cheese. "A change in the food, too," she added wryly. "I'll have to diet this week after all the glorious food I ate yesterday. Your mother's a wonderful cook."

"I hope you didn't have any ill effects." Wilma Christie smiled. "I'm afraid Mum assumes that all young people have enormous appetites — and as far as my brothers are concerned she's right.

"They don't have to watch their figures," she added, making a face, "so there's no dieting in our house."

Clare laughed at her work-mate's rueful expression.

"Well, I certainly enjoyed myself. It was very kind of you to ask me." She sipped her hot coffee slowly.

Wilma twisted her engagement ring nervously.

"I've been meaning to ask you for ages." She paused for a moment, then spoke again rather hesitantly. "Actually, I had a special reason for wanting you to meet my family.

"You see," she swallowed nervously, "I want to ask you a favour."

"Ask away then," Clare invited airily, with an encouraging smile.

"I'd like you to be my bridesmaid," Wilma said quietly.

The smile stiffened on Clare's face, as the words registered.

"But you hardly know me," she managed to reply, fighting down an urge to refuse loudly, sure that all the colour must have drained out of her face.

Wilma, seemingly unaware of the other girl's panic, replied apologetically.

"But we've been good friends ever since you came to the office." Then she continued confidingly, "I've never told you this before, Clare, but on the same day as you came to work here, Gavin asked me out for the first time.

"You know the rest." Wilma held out her engagement finger with its sparkling diamond. "We fell in love, and I'm afraid I haven't had much time for other friends since then."

Clare had recovered her poise but she could still hear the tremor in her own voice when she replied.

"But none of your friends would take offence about that," she said reasonably. "After all, it's only natural that you and Gavin like to be alone. Surely your girlfriends understand." She was aware of a pleading note in her voice. "There must be someone else you could ask to be bridesmaid — someone you know better."

Wilma's face flushed and she looked embarrassed as she tried to explain.

"That wasn't what I meant, Clare," she persisted. "I was trying to say that if Gavin hadn't come into my life at that particular time, then you and I would have probably spent more time together. After all," she finished, "you didn't know anyone at all when you first arrived."

Clare's reply was grateful.

"But thanks to you, Wilma, I've made quite a few friends now. I didn't think I'd have the courage to go to the Folk Club that first time," she went on, "even although you'd recommended it. But when Edna rang me up to say she'd be looking out for me — well I had to go, since you'd taken the trouble to phone her."

"It was no trouble," Wilma said quietly. Then with a glance at her watch, she rose to her feet, saying briskly, "Well, back to the typewriters."

CLARE realised afterwards that they hadn't returned to the subject of the wedding. She ought to have made it absolutely clear to Wilma that she had no intention of being her bridesmaid.

Why didn't I refuse more firmly? She asked herself the question, recalling the sheer panic which had assailed her at the very thought.

At the same time Clare told herself that a decisive shake of the head would have been enough. But, as usual, you shirked, she admitted to herself. When anything unpleasant happens you just run away.

Then the thought came into her mind that Wilma hadn't intended the question to be an unpleasant one. After all, it was an honour to be asked to be someone's bridesmaid.

Clare lifted her eyes reluctantly from her work, already starting to realise that she had hurt Wilma's feelings. And to her dismay she saw that the other girl's shoulders had a despondent droop and her expression was one of bewildered hurt.

But I can't help it, Clare sighed inwardly, knowing that it was most unlikely that she would ever be a bridesmaid again.

SHE'D worn a blue dress last time — it was probably still hanging in her wardrobe at home. Only she hadn't been home for six and a half months since she'd run away.

Well, she hadn't exactly run, she mused, but it had amounted to the same thing, even although she had taken the time to ask for the holiday due to her instead of working her notice. Then she'd spent three days helping her parents to pack and return her wedding presents before she packed her suitcases and left.

The blue dress, Clare thought sadly, had been the start of it all.

"You should wear blue always," had been the first words Jack ever said to her, transfixing her with his eyes, melting her heart.

He had been Simon's best man when she was Tina's bridesmaid. Love at first sight, everyone said, smiling indulgently, happily, on the whirlwind romance which had rushed Clare and Jack into an ecstatic engagement.

Their wedding would have been only eight months after Tina and Simon's.

In fact, Tina had agreed to be her matron of honour and Simon was to be Jack's best man . . .

Tight memories of pain pulled at Clare's heart as she recalled Jack's miserable features when he had told her that he'd met someone else, that he wanted to postpone their wedding.

Pride had forced Clare to give him his freedom, but not the freedom to make a choice between herself and the other girl. The break was final as far as she was concerned.

In her heart, though, she had believed that Jack was the only man she would ever love. But Jack's love had been fickle while hers was not, and knowing the agony of heart she would suffer if she saw him with the other girl, Clare had swiftly put as much distance as she could between them.

BUT distance had not healed her aching heart, and neither had time. She still mourned constantly for the loss of her love; every night, she looked at the photograph of herself and Jack gazing tenderly into each other's eyes . . .

Clare's thoughts stopped there. Her fingers on the typewriter keys fumbled and came to a stop. She hadn't looked at the photograph on Sunday night, she'd been too tired. But the night before? No, she'd come in late from a party.

She distinctly remembered setting her alarm clock for nine so she would be up in plenty of time to do her laundry before she went to Wilma's home for Sunday dinner. But she couldn't remember looking at the photograph.

Friday night, then? She tried to cast her mind back but her memory was refusing to function. Her thoughts were spinning off in all directions. Mixing with her efforts to recall Jack's face was the recollection of the warm welcome she had received at the Christies' house the day before.

Wilma's parents had been charming, as had Wilma's two brothers.

Gavin, she knew, of course, because he worked for the same firm. But it had been pleasant to meet him socially, as Wilma's fiancé, instead of the business-like person he was in the office.

Altogether Clare had spent a most enjoyable day at her friend's home. With a pang of sadness, she thought now of Mr and Mrs Christie smiling and waving goodbye and urging her to come back soon. They were so nice.

Do You Remember?

DO you remember springtime, not so
many years ago,
When our hearts were young and our
steps were light
And our eyes were all aglow?
Do you remember feeling, not so many
years ago,
A joy so great that had to shout
To let the whole world know?
Do you remember being in love, not so
many years ago,
With a heart so full, beating so fast
You thought it must surely show?

I remember all these things, my love,
And I keep them in my heart,
But these memories of a youth gone by
Were really just the start,
Of a love much more than a fleeting
thing,
A love that's deep and true,
A love that brings contentment,
A love that's built around you.
And when our children fall in love,
As I am sure they will,
I hope they'll find a love like ours,
A love that's growing still.

Barbara Cheshire.

At lunch-time, Clare caught a glimpse of Wilma whisking swiftly out of the office, then at the afternoon tea-break Wilma vanished for the full ten minutes. Later, Clare noticed that the other girl covered her typewriter and hurried out ten minutes early. Obviously Wilma had decided to avoid Clare.

Neither of us knows how to handle a situation like this, Clare thought morosely.

Maybe it was just as well that she had until tomorrow.

WHILE she ate her solitary meal in her bedsitter, Clare was debating with herself whether or not to go to see Wilma that evening.

The old, familiar photograph of Jack and herself was propped up in front of her as she ate, but as she gazed at it there were no tears in her eyes, no gnawing pain in her heart.

"Some day you'll realise that he wasn't good enough for you," her mother had comforted her as Clare had wept. "Try not to be bitter, dear. Believe me, this is all for the best."

Running away had been her answer, but she couldn't run away now. She would have to face Wilma. Maybe not with the whole story, but at least part of it, enough to make the other girl understand.

Slowly, Clare put the photograph away in the drawer, knowing that her bruised heart had finally healed. She wished that the knowledge had brought some pleasure instead of the odd sensation of emptiness which she felt, a forlorn freedom which made her want to sit down and cry.

But that was ridiculous, she told herself sternly, and swiftly making up her mind, Clare began to get ready to go to the orchestral concert for which she had bought a ticket.

MUSIC, she decided, was exactly what was needed to calm her troubled mind. Later, she would decide on how best to explain to Wilma.

Although Clare had a reasonably good social life and had made some new friends, she always made a habit of going to concerts by herself.

That night, during the interval she remained in her seat, unwilling to be distracted from the mood of the concert.

At the end, as she made her way to the exit, she was conscious of a warm, mellow glow pervading her being.

"Small world, isn't it?" A voice beside her remarked. "Did you enjoy the concert, Clare?"

Clare was still in the thrall of the music as she raised bemused eyes to the speaker's face. She blinked in astonishment as she recognised Wilma's brother.

"Hello, Peter." She smilingly agreed that, indeed, it was a small world.

They stood talking for a few moments, exchanging comments about the concert. Clare could see that he was a music lover like herself.

"Look, we can't just stand here chatting." Peter smiled ruefully as he moved to let someone past. "How about coming with me for a cup of coffee, something to eat?" he suggested. "Then we could continue our conversation."

Clare's hesitation was only momentary. She was surprised to find that she liked the idea — surprised to find herself accepting.

Just before they left the restaurant, Peter looked steadily into her eyes.

"I wanted to meet you again, Clare," he admitted. "I'm glad I set up that accidental meeting."

Taken aback, Clare was unable to think of anything to say. But then, as he seemed to be waiting for her reaction, she moved her hands in a helpless gesture.

"But why?" was all she could think of to say.

Peter inclined his head, as if to indicate that the answer to that was too obvious.

"Because you are an extremely attractive girl, of course," he murmured.

Blushing slightly under the obvious admiration in his eyes, Clare chose her words carefully.

"I suppose I meant — why an accidental meeting? Or maybe I meant how did you arrange it?"

"It nearly went wrong, I almost missed you!" Peter grinned boyishly. "I had to push my way quite ruthlessly to your side, and elbowing people aside is just not the done thing among the decorous devotees of orchestral concerts!"

"I'd have looked for you if I'd known you were going to be there," she assured him.

There was a small silence following her remark, and her smile slowly disappeared.

"Would you really have?" Peter's features wore an earnest look of appeal. "I mean, if I'd asked you yesterday, would you have let me take you to the concert?"

Instead of answering his questions, Clare regarded him with perplexed eyes.

"What makes you think I would have refused?" she asked. "I don't understand what you mean."

"Neither do I, really," he confessed. "Now that we've met again — accidentally — I can hardly believe that you were so unapproachable when you visited us yesterday."

"Unapproachable?" Clare swallowed hard at his choice of word.

"Well, you didn't seem to be, shall we say, receptive to my charms?" Peter was finding it difficult to express himself. "You seemed as if you wanted to give the impression that you already had a boyfriend, someone special."

SUDDENLY, Peter looked uncertain and anxious, as if he were wishing that he could take back the words he had just spoken.

Guessing that he must have asked his sister about her and discovered that there was no boyfriend in the offing, Clare was acutely conscious of his present embarrassment. He had said too much, too soon, but that wasn't important.

What mattered was that there was a wonderful rapport between them and it would be a shame to spoil it at the very beginning.

"I don't know why I gave that impression, Peter. There's nobody else," she spoke softly, responding to the appeal in his eyes.

He made no attempt to conceal his satisfaction. Yet, as his hand reached out to touch Clare's, an intuitive knowledge prompted him to choose his words carefully.

"But there used to be someone . . . wasn't there. Clare?"

Memory of Jack was a gradually fading image and she blotted it out once and for all with her reply.

"Yes, I was engaged to be married, but the wedding was called off at the eleventh hour."

"I'm sorry." He squeezed her hand in swift sympathy.

The smile that Clare gave him was unexpectedly brilliant.

"Don't be!" she cried. "It's past and forgotten now. My mother was right when she said it was all for the best."

She knew that she would never forget the heartbreaking experience she had suffered, although remembering was less painful already.

I N the morning Clare overslept and had a wild rush to be at the office on time. Hurrying into the cloakroom with less than two minutes to spare, she was startled to find Wilma there, waiting for her.

With an air of determination, Wilma faced her friend.

"Clare, I want to say . . ."

"And I want to apologise," Clare interrupted quickly. "I'm truly sorry I went into such a panic when you asked me to be your bridesmaid."

"If you don't want to, it's quite all right," Wilma answered, but Clare could see she was unhappy about it.

"Wilma, don't look so solemn!" she commanded cheerfully. "Of course I want to be your bridesmaid. It's just that you took my breath away when you asked me yesterday, out of the blue!"

"Are you sure?" An expression of relief lit up Wilma's face. "Do you *really* want to?"

"I'm sure." Clare nodded her head emphatically. "We're liable to be in trouble if we stand here talking any longer, though!"

Clare sat down at her desk, her thoughts in a turmoil. Until a minute ago, she'd really had no intention of agreeing to be her friend's bridesmaid. She couldn't think why she had agreed. And yet — she was glad.

G AVIN came into the main office, and watching him as he stopped to speak to Wilma, aware of the look of love which they exchanged, Clare's breath caught in her throat.

She knew this wasn't the first time she'd seen that look, but before she'd kept her emotions well in check, and ignored them. But today she felt different, somehow.

Unapproachable, Peter had said she was. Now, visualising Peter's smile, the warm admiration in his eyes, Clare couldn't suppress a delicious flutter of excitement.

Just at the right moment of time in her life, Peter had made her start to think of the future, her thoughts ran on. On Sunday afternoon, she had perhaps been more impressed by Peter's charm than either of them realised . . .

The meeting that he had engineered would have taken place one way or another, Clare decided. And she was meeting him again at seven o'clock tonight! □

No-One To Turn To

by
Laura
Caldwell

THAT morning, just as she did every morning, Violet Watson
nodded to Victoria as she passed her on the stairs. As always,
Vickie was looking very sweet in her day-dress of plum bombazine, pink-frilled pinafore, and button shoes of soft white kid. Her
golden ringlets were caught in a velvet ribbon, and a necklace of tiny
red glass beads — the very beads Kenneth had found in a cracker one
Christmas when he was a schoolboy — encircled her neck. Her cheeks
were palest rose-colour and her wide-open eyes forget-me-not blue.

"Yes, yes, you're a beauty!" Violet murmured, as she went on down
to prepare her breakfast. Easy to be so serene and beautiful, she
thought, when all you had to do all day was sit in your own special

chair set in the landing window-sill, half-way up and half-way down the staircase of Hawthorn House!

Yes, a pleasant life indeed for little Miss Victoria. Mrs Watson's hands shook as she put on an egg to boil. But then, why not? Surely she didn't grudge her beautiful doll a trouble-free existence? After all, tomorrow Vickie would be one hundred and twenty-five years old!

THE letter-box rattled. It was the post! Mrs Watson's heart was thudding before she reached the hall. Two envelopes; bills both of them. Without opening them she knew that one was the final reminder from the town hall about the rates; the other was the electricity account, second time round!

Well, they must both wait till she had her tea and toast and egg!

The truth was since Jim had died, four years ago this coming spring, things had been hard indeed for his widow.

The first blow had come right away with the lawyer's question.

"You are aware of the state of your husband's business, Mrs Watson?"

No. She had not known anything. Jim had always been one to keep business matters to himself. She knew the bookshop had been badly hit, like many of the other shops, when their small town was by-passed by the new motorway.

But Violet had been shocked when the lawyer had continued.

"The fact is the business owes more money than it has. We might just break even with the sale of the stock — but even then . . ." He had looked doubtful.

Violet had been shaken. It appeared her husband had left debts and little else.

POOR dear Jim. She didn't blame him. He had been a loving husband, protecting her always from life's harsher side. Maybe she should have taken more interest in the shop — but then he had never wanted that, the business was strictly his concern.

If they'd had a son, a bright lad to step in and help his father and eventually take over the shop . . . but Violet and Jim Watson had had no family.

There had been Kenneth, of course. These days Violet found herself thinking often about her nephew, Kenneth, wondering about him. It had been a real blow that he and Jim had not seen eye to eye about his career. Jim had wanted him to take over the shop.

"I'm not all that interested in books, Uncle Jim," he'd said. "I'm a science man. I'm sorry, but I wouldn't be any good at it."

"But, Kenneth —" The discussions and arguments had gone on endlessly, but to no avail.

The Watsons had been good to Kenneth. He had spent all his holidays with them, for his own parents had died tragically in Africa. It was Jim Watson who had taught him to fish and birdwatch; they had bought him his first bicycle, encouraged him at school.

In return, the boy — for Kenneth Blackie was naturally affectionate

— had given generously of his love. So that Jim Watson was shattered when he turned down the offer of a partnership in Watson's Bookshop.

Jim had never really recovered from the disappointment. In his university days Kenneth Blackie came less and less to Hawthorn House. When he did come there was a strained atmosphere and sometimes angry words.

Violet did her best. She loved her nephew but she loved Jim, too, and she felt torn apart.

Kenneth took a post in a college in New Zealand and, gradually, as the years went by, they lost touch.

The strange thing was, though, that this Christmas card had arrived right out of the blue.

It was a mounted, coloured snapshot of Kenneth — an older, very distinguished-looking Kenneth — sitting on a garden bench with a pretty young woman and a chubby little girl.

Happy Christmas dear Auntie Violet, from Kenneth, Valerie and Wendy. Look out for a letter very soon, it said. There was no address. Just a Wellington postmark.

Violet had been excited. Fancy Kenneth married and with a bonnie wee girl of his own! She had looked eagerly for the promised letter, but the weeks passed and nothing came. And so, once more she tried to put Kenneth to the back of her mind.

THE sudden ringing of the doorbell made her jump. Really, she must get out of this habit of day-dreaming, of deliberately harking back to the past. She opened the front door — it was Sandy Barr about the roof.

"I've brought you our estimate, Vi." He held out an envelope.

She asked him to come in.

"Do you want a cup of tea?"

Violet had known Sandy Barr and his brothers since they were all children. The Barr brothers had been slaters in the town for generations, and had a prosperous business indeed. Violet had asked them to have a look at her roof. Hawthorn House was old and water was coming through the ceiling of the back bedroom. She realised Sandy was speaking to her.

"Your roof's in a bad way," he said. "Another winter like last and I wouldn't like to say what might happen. But the good news is we can start work next week."

A FEW minutes later, on his way out, Sandy stood at the open door looking down on her.

"How do you fancy going to a concert on Saturday, Violet? I could get a couple of good seats — would you like that?"

Sandy Barr loved music, and he knew Violet shared this love.

"What do you say, eh?" His kind brown eyes were pleading.

It was tempting. Sandy was a good friend. When Jim was ill in hospital he had often run her back and forward to Aberdeen to visit him.

Now she reflected how restful it would be to sit beside him in the darkened hall listening to the visiting orchestra. Perhaps then she would forget her worries for a little while.

"Thank you, Sandy, I'd love to go." She smiled gratefully.

Her old friend was delighted. He turned his attention to the doll. He took off his cap and made a sweeping bow towards the stairs.

"Good morning to you, Victoria! My, but you're looking bonnie!" he called.

They were the words he would have liked to say to Violet Watson, but he was a shy man.

"You've had her a long time, Vi," he said, instead.

"My great-grandmother was given her on her tenth birthday, Sandy, so that makes Vickie one hundred and twenty-five years old."

"That's a good age," he murmured, staring with wonder at the beautiful doll.

Later, as he drove away from Hawthorn Cottage in his van, Sandy Barr was uneasy. Something was wrong with Violet Watson! He had thought so all winter, and now he was certain.

He wished she would confide in him — maybe she was ill and didn't want folk to know, maybe she was just plain lonely or perhaps it was money worries.

Anyway, he reflected happily, she had accepted his invitation.

I'll make sure she has a really good night out! he promised himself.

WHEN Sandy had gone, Violet busied herself about the house. She tried to ignore the three unopened envelopes now propped on the mantelpiece.

"I'll open them after dinner," she decided — but by late afternoon the envelopes were still there undisturbed!

"I'll open them as soon as I've had my tea —"

Even in the midst of her mounting worries Violet Watson's sense of humour did not desert her.

"You're just like an ostrich," she told herself out loud, "hiding your silly old head in the sand.

"Open them now!" And she did.

In seconds her poor heart was thudding like the drums of doom. She had been right about the rates:

"Unless the above sum is paid at once, etc., etc."

Oh, it was humiliating!

The electricity folk pointed out this was the second account they had submitted and unless, etc., etc. And Barr Brothers estimate for the roof was one hundred and fifty pounds!

The little widow slumped down on a chair. What was she to do? If she had found a part-time job that would have helped. However, East Moray was a very small town, and there were few jobs going begging, and certainly none for a woman of fifty-nine, who had no special skills.

Her gloomy thoughts were interrupted by the doorbell ringing. She thought it might be the minister. Mr McLeod was a regular visitor and a good friend. But she'd been unable to confide in him, either.

Violet wished she had someone of her own to turn to.

H OWEVER, it wasn't the minister who stood in the driving rain on her doorstep.

"Good afternoon, Mrs Watson. You'll remember me?" With a charming smile the young man handed her a card. It was the travelling antique dealer from Aberdeen, once again on his rounds.

Violet's reply was automatic.

"I'm afraid I've nothing —"

"No? Ah well — " He shook the rain from his head.

"Do you think I might come out of this storm for a minute?"

He was polite, a likeable fellow. Mrs Watson stood aside to let him enter.

She knew the man quite well — he'd been coming round the doors of East Moray for years, always looking for old brass, Victorian jewellery, copper jelly-pans.

Once, years ago, when Jim was alive, they had sold him a pair of unwanted wally dugs.

So after that the antique man had called each time he was in the town.

"That doll —" He was nodding towards the stair landing.

"Do you mind if I have a closer look?"

"No, no, go up."

The antique dealer went swiftly upstairs. For a long moment he was silent, inspecting the doll at close quarters. Then, with careful hands, he lifted her.

"May I bring her down?"

It was growing dusk.

"We'll go into the living-room, shall we? You can see her properly in there."

T HEY sat on opposite sides of the fire, the man intent on every detail of the doll.

"She's perfect," Violet told him with great pride.

"You won't find a single flaw in my Victoria."

"I can see that. She's French, of course. I'm almost certain she's French —"

He was very excited. This was a perfect example of the doll-maker's skill. The head of finest bisque, the eyes of brilliant blue glass, the body of best white kid. Not one tiny finger was missing from the doll's hands. Only the plum bombazine was faded now with time. He was an honest man and he did not beat about the bush. "I'd like to buy this," he said, bluntly. And when he made his offer Violet Watson could hardly believe her ears. All that money for a doll.

"It's a very fair offer," the young man said. "You won't get a better one anywhere else," he persuaded.

Mrs Watson had had no idea. Fancy all that money for a doll, for a child's toy! She remained silent, but her thoughts ran ahead . . .

Such a sum would clear those menacing bills at one stroke, there might even be a little left to put aside. The widow felt a gradual lifting of her spirits. It was like a miracle. She hesitated no longer.

"All right," she heard her voice say.

SANDY BARR was worried about his friend, Violet. She sat beside him in the front row of the balcony in the town hall, the very best seats. It was the interval and he had just presented her with a box of chocolates.

"All creams," he whispered. "I remembered you had a weakness for cream chocolates."

She had smiled, then.

"Oh, Sandy, thank you." She'd been grateful. "But you shouldn't, you . . ." That was as far as she got.

Sandy was dismayed to see Violet's gentle grey eyes brim with tears. Something was very wrong tonight. She had been as quiet as a mouse from the word go, her mind so obviously on other things, and not happy things either.

She tried to pull herself together, but she found she just couldn't. She could think of nothing but Vickie!

The curious thing was Violet Watson had not fully realised what she had done, until two whole days after she saw Victoria being carried away by the antique dealer!

She had hurried to settle the bills, the rates, the electricity, and had banked the remainder against the roof repair.

Her fantastic feelings of relief had lasted until the third morning when, coming downstairs, the price she had paid for her relief suddenly hit her like a body blow.

GOOD NEWS

THANK the postman bringing you your mail.

Slips it through the letter-box, in weather fair or foul. Times you wait his coming. Is he stopping at your door with the letter you so eagerly await?

Your daughter's baby safely born; your sister's booked her passage from Canada in June.

Thank the postie also for other happy things: Your niece become engaged; letter from a girlhood friend, with memories of long ago. Your grandchild's brief untidy scrawl – drawn a pussy at the top, put kisses at the foot.

But when you visit some solitary soul, share an hour with her, don't you play the postman?

Slip through the letter-box into some lonely soul – a note of happiness!

Rev. T. R. S. Campbell.

The little basket-chair on the window-shelf was empty, the beautiful doll which had been part of her life, of her mother's life, her grandmother's and great-grandmother's, had gone forever!

Now the orchestra had struck up the National Anthem, the concert was at an end. But Violet Watson seemed lost to everything but her own sad thoughts.

Fifteen minutes later Sandy Barr turned the key in the lock of Hawthorn House, but when Mrs Watson made to go in, he firmly held her back, determined to get to the root of the problem.

"There's something bothering you, Vi. What is it?"

Out poured the whole sorry story. The near-bankrupt bookshop, the succession of bills.

"There seemed no end to it all, Sandy," she said, sorrowfully.

Sandy Barr shook his head.

"Woman, it's high time you had someone looking after you!"

Then a minute later:

"That antique dealer, is it the same man who always comes about East Moray?"

"He gave me a card." She fetched it now from the mantelpiece and showed it to Sandy.

"Now listen to me, Violet. As it just happens, I've a business appointment in Aberdeen come Monday morning. I'll see what I can do." He nodded in a shy sort of way, but said no more.

As he drove back to his own trim — but lonely — house on the outskirts of the town, Sandy Barr knew exactly what he was going to do!

I'M sorry sir, that Victorian doll was on display just a couple of days when it was sold."

Sandy could hardly believe his ears. He had been so confident the doll was his for the asking, so certain he would be calling in at Hawthorn House that very evening with Vickie safe under his arm.

He could not leave the antique shop without a last try.

"I suppose you wouldn't tell me the name of the buyer?"

The shop-owner shook his head.

"That would be against our rules, sir. It is something we never do. But we'll keep our eyes open for another Victorian doll. They are, of course, rare on the market, especially such a perfect example as that one was, however it may be —"

This time it was Sandy's turn to shake his head. He was interested only in Mrs Watson's doll, and now it seemed all his money couldn't buy it back.

The antique dealer, watching his disappointed customer leave, was intrigued. The quiet man from East Moray was plainly upset at having been too late. Why?

And why had the younger man who bought the Victorian doll a few days ago been so desperately eager to get it? The staff had noticed the gentleman staring, staring into the window where the doll was displayed among the ginger jars, rosy tea-sets and Victorian jewellery.

Later, coming into the shop, he had paid willingly the substantial price asked. Perhaps it was a trick of the muted lighting within the shop, but Mr Dalrymple had imagined the man's face drained of colour as he held the doll, touching almost reverently the faded pinafore, the necklace of tiny glass beads . . . Intriguing, very intriguing!

SANDY was reluctant to confess his unhappy news to Violet. He arrived at her house on Tuesday morning with his apprentice, and right away they started on the roof repairs.

When five o'clock came and the lad had gone off home, Sandy could avoid it no longer.

"I tried, Vi," he told her, apologetically. "I was shattered when they told me it had gone."

He tried to avoid looking at her strained face and sad eyes.

"You're a dear, good friend, Sandy," she said, tenderly. "You've gone to a lot of trouble for a stupid old woman. Thank you."

"You're neither stupid nor old, Violet Watson," he said angrily. "Would I want to marry you so much if you were!" He stopped, then, horrified at the way he'd blurted out his feelings.

"Words don't come easy to me, Vi, and I'm forever dithering. But I'm very fond of you, and I'd do anything to help."

Violet Watson's sensitive nature was shaken by Sandy's sudden declaration. She was sure he was offering help now, only because he was sorry for her.

Only later, as she locked her door against the dark night, did the tears come, tears of regret for the loss of her doll and for so hastily turning her back on her dear friend.

A T ten minutes to eight that same night the doorbell of Hawthorn House rang firmly. Violet had very few uninvited visitors in the evenings and so she was surprised and even a little alarmed.

"Who is it please?" she called.

But the stout door muffled sounds although the voice was clearly a male one. Cautiously she lifted the safety-latch and, keeping the chain securely in place, opened the door a few inches.

"Hello, Auntie Violet!" The young man smiled.

Violet Watson could scarcely believe the evidence of her own eyes. "Kenneth!"

"Aren't you going to let me in, Auntie Vi?" he asked, with a laugh.

How they talked! There seemed to be no end to all they had to say.

"That Christmas card, Kenneth, oh, I was so pleased to get it . . . but your letter never came!" she exclaimed.

"I didn't forget, I meant to write, then out of the blue I got the offer of this job in Aberdeen, so . . ." He broke off.

"I decided not to write and tell you we were coming, but just drop in and give you a surprise!"

Oh, he was still the same happy, smiling Kenneth.

"You'll bring Valerie to see me?" she asked excitedly.

"And Wendy!" he added. "Wait till you see little Wendy, she's a real charmer. How about tomorrow?"

"Come for tea, all of you." She hadn't felt so happy in a long time.

Violet scarcely slept a wink that night. But hers was a happy restlessness and by morning she was bursting to share her wonderful news with someone and Sandy's was the first name that came into her mind. She would tell him when he arrived, to fix the roof. He'd said he would come at eight o'clock.

And he did! He listened with shining eyes while Vi poured out her story.

"And you'll join us for tea, Sandy? Of course you will. Mercy me, you knew Kenneth nearly as well as we did!"

MRS WATSON spent the day planning and preparing food for her party. She made a jelly in the shape of a rabbit for the wee girl . . . Thinking of Kenneth's little girl made her think of toys, and toys made her think of Vickie, the precious doll!

Once again a great wave of regret swept over Violet, nearly — but not quite — sweeping away her present happiness. If only Vickie was still there, seated on the window ledge for Wendy to play with and love . . .

Later, seeing them all seated round her table, Violet Watson's heart was full. There was Kenneth, her handsome nephew, his pretty New Zealand wife, Valerie, and three-year-old Wendy, a rosy-cheeked adorable little girl.

And then, because of the years of loneliness, the hard-up, difficult years, tears came into Violet's gentle eyes.

"Maybe you'll be surprised to hear this isn't all of us, Auntie Vi. As a matter of fact we've left another member of the family sitting outside in the car!"

Kenneth pushed back his chair.

"It's growing chilly," he said. "I'd better fetch her in. Come and help me, Wendy poppet."

"It's a secret su'prise for you, Auntie Vi'let!"

And they were off out of the room like a couple of conspirators.

WHEN they had left, Valerie spoke to Violet.

"You've no idea what Ken's been like since Christmas," she said. "He's been as excited as a schoolboy about coming home, being close to East Moray, Hawthorn House and you."

There was a loud knocking at the living-room door.

"Here comes the su'prise! Here comes the secret!"

And Kenneth held the door wide to let Wendy through. Wendy came in, proudly carrying Victoria, holding the beautiful doll with careful small hands.

Before the astounded Violet could say anything, Ken placed his clenched fist before her.

"Guess what this pretty thing is?" he asked.

Then he spread out his hand to reveal the necklace of tiny red beads Victoria had worn for years.

"This was the first thing that caught my eye when I saw Vickie in the Aberdeen shop. I spotted the necklace, *my* necklace — remember, Aunt Vi, I got it out of a cracker one Christmas? Then I knew it just must be our Vickie! I knew, too, that some miraculous power had led my footsteps to that antique shop, so, in I went and here she is!"

For a while all Violet Watson could say was:

"She's come home, Vickie's come home!"

In such a short time her whole life had changed. All the past unhappiness had been swept away. She looked around at her "new" family. And when her eyes stopped at Sandy, their eyes met hastily and she looked away, but not before she'd seen his smile of pleasure.

Yes, the future looked like being very happy indeed. □

You've Only Yourselves To Blame

By Phyllis Heath

"**P**ERHAPS you should put up a plaque," Chris suggested to her mother as they stood together in the almost bare bedroom. Only the girl's old dressing-gown hung behind the door, and her brushes still there on the dressing-table, spoke of the room's use.

Everything else, all the tiny personal belongings that Chris treasured, had been packed away.

"You know the short of thing — *Christine slept here*." Chris was trying to lighten a tense moment.

Dutifully Brenda Wainwright laughed, but her laughter had a hollow ring to it, even to her own ears.

"It seems so strange to think you won't be using this room again." She excused her lack of amusement. "After nearly twenty-one years."

Brenda's eyes grew wistful as her thoughts travelled back down those years. Back to the day when she had carried her tiny baby daughter into this very room.

IT hadn't looked bare then, with its wallpaper of blue and pink animals, and its gaily-decorated white furniture. There had been yellow curtains at the window then, and a yellow, fluffy rug in the middle of the floor.

Brenda had decided on yellow and white when she first found she was pregnant.

"It might be a boy or a girl," she had told Martin very seriously, and he had laughed at her with his eyes, though his face had remained solemn.

"It'll probably be one or the other, I should think," he had agreed.

"Now, Martin." Brenda had giggled. "You know what I mean!" Then he had caught her up in a bear-like hug.

"Of course I do!" He had laughed happily. "Paint it any colour you want. Do anything that makes you happy, my clever darling. That's all I want." He had kissed her cheek lovingly. Then he had let her slide gently down to the floor.

"I'll have to stop fooling around like this, won't I?" he had asked, and Brenda had sensed the regret in his words.

"Just for a little while," she had answered.

But Martin had never really grown out of his boisterous, boyish ways. He had never lost his bouncy, noisy way of walking, nor had he stopped singing loudly in the bath, or his way of shouting their names the moment he entered the house.

Not until that evening when Chris had come home and said she wanted to marry Patrick . . .

A FTER that night, it was as if the joy of living had drained out of her husband. Like a deflated balloon, he was the same but different — still made of the same materials but no longer effervescent.

Brenda had had the first inkling of how it would be with Martin when he had stared back at his daughter, his face falling, his hands hanging limply, as he almost whispered what she had just told them.

"Patrick Drake?" He had looked amazed. "You want to marry Patrick Drake? But he's . . . It *is* the same man? It *is* the Patrick Drake who works with me?"

Chris had nodded and her father had gone on to describe this man who was to become his son-in-law.

"The man I have lunch with on pay day?" Martin had gone on. "The lad who used to hang around me when I played rugby for the club?"

Chris had merely nodded once more in agreement.

"But he's nearly as old as me!" At last Martin had put into words exactly what he had against her choice.

"It doesn't matter." Chris had looked at her father with pleading eyes. "Dad, it doesn't matter."

"But it does matter!" Martin had glared at her. "Haven't you any sense?" For a moment there had been a glimpse of the old Martin, but it had quickly disappeared.

"I love him, Dad." Chris had turned to Brenda, "Mum, make him understand."

B UT Brenda hadn't been able to do that. She hadn't understood herself.

"You hardly know him." She had brushed aside Chris's protest that Patrick had been a friend of the family for years. "I mean, you haven't met him as a friend, been out with him."

"We didn't want to keep it from you, Mum, but we guessed how it would be." Chris had lowered her gaze. "We've been going out for some months and Patrick wants to get engaged. We thought we should tell you first."

"So you did see we'd have reason to object," Martin had accused her. If they could see that much, all might not be lost. "Look, love, Patrick's what — twenty years older than you?"

"Eighteen," Chris had corrected her father.

You've Only Yourselves To Blame

"He's middle aged now. He'll be an old man when you're still like your mother. Look at her, Chris!" he had commanded. "Just look at her — she's attractive, she likes to go out and about, wear nice clothes.

"She plays badminton and tennis with me, we go dancing and hiking and . . . oh, all sorts of things. We do these things together." He had tried so hard to convince his daughter.

"But what if I was going on sixty-five? What then? Maybe I'd want to sit around a bit, watch television . . ."

Martin's voice had risen, but it wasn't the same as when he raised it in laughter or greeting. Now he was angry, and Chris had a temper to match her father's.

I DON'T care! I don't care!" she had shouted. "I love Patrick and I don't want anyone else. I want to marry him. You can't stop me. You can't make me change my mind."

Brenda had tried to soothe Chris.

"It's not like that, love. We only want you to be happy. Dad's only pointing out the difficulties.

"Marriage is difficult enough, any marriage," she had gone on. "Why make it harder on yourself? You've got to think about these things."

"We have. Don't you think Patrick's told me all these things?" Chris had grown calmer now.

"Huh! I'm glad to see he's not a complete idiot," Martin had retorted.

"I thought you liked him — he's always been a friend, been welcome here." The defiant note had come back into Chris's voice.

"He'll not be . . ." Martin had started to speak when Brenda's cry stopped the words.

"Don't say it. There must be a way. There must be something we can say — Chris?"

But there was nothing they *could* say which would change the girl's mind.

I T'S my life, Mum," she had told her mother next day when they were alone. "You always told me to live my own life, you and Dad.

"Don't you remember, when I was little and came home saying I wanted to do something because everyone else was doing it?" She had smiled at the memory. "You used to ask, 'Chris, who are you?'

"You used to say that if I wanted it because I was me, and *I* wanted to do it, then you'd discuss whatever it was. But if I just wanted to because everyone else was doing it, then you weren't interested." Brenda had recalled those moments well as her daughter had continued.

"Well this is what I want, because I'm *me* — you must see that . . ." There had been a certain logic in the argument.

So though Brenda and Martin couldn't like what had happened, Chris was their daughter and they could never let her down.

51

But though they had tried to joke, and say all the right things to Chris and Patrick, they had found it difficult.

In one way Brenda was glad that they'd only another day to get through — tomorrow was Chris's wedding day.

STANDING together now in the bedroom it was as if Chris had sensed her mother's thoughts. She put an arm round her, laying her cheek against Brenda's.

"Don't worry, Mum, it'll be all right," she said. "Patrick loves me, he really does. And in some ways I'm luckier than lots of girls." She moved across to the dressing-table and picked up her hair-brush. "Look at the house I'm moving into — no cottage for us, no waiting until we've saved up for the washing-machine and the fridge." A smile lit up her features. "And you know how I love babies, we won't have to wait for them either."

Brenda stifled the protest which leapt to her lips, thinking that by the time any children were in their teens Patrick might seem like an old man to them.

Instead, she walked across the room and hugged her daughter.

"We just want you to be happy." She turned to the suitcases, ready and waiting in the corner. "Everything packed?" she queried. "You haven't forgotten anything?"

"No, I'm sure I've not." Chris looked over at the cases, too. "Patrick's going out tonight with his friends, so I can have an early night." She crossed over to the door with her mother. "There seems to have been so much to do, doesn't there?"

"Weddings are like that." Brenda smiled. "But everything's ready now and an early night will do us all good." They went downstairs together. "I think Dad's a bit nervous. You know, Chris, he's never had to make a speech before!"

"Not Dad — nothing frightens him," Chris protested. But it was a ritual protest, she knew her father hadn't been his usual self lately. It hurt to think she was the cause of it, but there was nothing she could do. Perhaps when he sees how happy Patrick and I are, he'll come round, she consoled herself.

THEY had an early meal and watched television for a time but Martin was restless and couldn't concentrate.

"I think I'll take a book up to bed," he finally decided. "I don't seem to be able to settle down."

Brenda began to punch up the cushions and tidy up, her mood matching his.

"I won't be long, so I'll bring a hot drink when I come upstairs."

Chris jumped up to kiss her father as he got up out of his chair.

" 'Night, Dad. Don't lose any sleep over me — I'm a big girl now." But her voice wobbled slightly. Her mother recognised that Chris's flippancy was merely a camouflage for her feelings. She hoped Martin would understand.

"I know, my dear, I know." He turned when he reached the door.

"Don't ever forget where we live, will you?" His voice was quiet. "This will always be your home."

With moist eyes Chris watched her father leave the room, and when Brenda asked her, she agreed she would have a cup of chocolate and get to bed too.

MARTIN was reading with an intentness which didn't deceive Brenda when she finally came into the room. She put his cup down on the bedside table and began to prepare for bed.

"She'll be all right, love," she reassured him. "You've got to stop worrying about her."

"*I've* got to stop worrying?" Martin took his eyes away from his book. "What about you?" He took her hand as she settled beside him.

"I don't suppose parents ever really stop worrying about their children. My own father used to make me despair the way he worried about me, and I was a lot older than Chris."

"Once a parent always a parent," Brenda agreed.

There was silence in the room for quite a time. They were both keen readers and loved the half-hour before sleep claimed them each night. But generally Brenda found that her eyes grew heavy and she was almost asleep before she had put the book aside and turned out the light. Tonight, however, she appeared to be getting more and more awake.

"I'll look terrible to-morrow," she said despondently. "What will be the use of my new hair-do, and that expensive dress, if I've got bags under my eyes?" she demanded. "I must try to sleep."

"I suppose you're right." Martin switched off the light on his side and they snuggled down. "Per-haps I should have gone out with Patrick and his mates after all, then I might have got to sleep more easily," he grumbled.

So In Love

I WONDER why the grass looks greener,
And all the springtime flowers smell sweeter,
I wonder why the hours fly fleeter,
When two people fall in love.

I wonder why the sky seems bluer,
And the land so fresh and newer,
I wonder, could two hearts beat truer
Than do ours, my dearest love.

But why miss magic, thus to ponder,
With each golden day so full of wonder,
And we two growing ever fonder
Of each other, O my love!

—*Violet Hull.*

"Well, I didn't stop you," Brenda said, as if she thought he was accusing her.

"I know, love." His fingers touched hers. "Perhaps all parents lie awake on nights like this."

"I suppose they do," Brenda agreed, but she knew it wasn't quite the same in their case.

They didn't speak again, each busy with their own thoughts, until a strange scratching noise alerted Brenda.

L ISTEN! There's someone on the landing," she whispered, nudging Martin.

"It's only Chris," he murmured sleepily. "Go to sleep."

"It can't be Chris, she wouldn't creep about like that." Brenda stared at the door. "There's no light either. Why wouldn't she put the light on?" she demanded. "Perhaps she's upset and needs me."

Instantly Brenda was out of bed and padding towards the door, but by the time she reached it her eyes had got used to the dark and she could see something white on the carpet, just peeping under the door.

"There's something here." She picked up the paper and took it towards the bed, switching on the small light as she did so. "It's a note, I think. It's addressed to both of us."

Her gaze went to Martin, who was now fully awake as his wife unfolded the sheets of notepaper. "It's from Chris!"

Brenda smiled as she got back into bed and snuggled against Martin.

"What a nice thing to do. I expect she realised we wouldn't have much time together tomorrow, there'll be all those people at the wedding. I suppose she wants to say thank you, in her own way."

Her eyes scanned the first few lines of Chris's letter and her voice faltered when she spoke again.

"It's not really that — I'm not sure what it is." She read on further. "She's not really saying thank you . . ."

"Read it out, love," Martin suggested. "Perhaps then we'll both understand."

Brenda began to read, picturing Chris sitting up in bed busily scribbling. Chris had always kept up with her friends, even when they moved away, and she loved to write letters. Brenda had often gone into her room to find her asleep over her writing pad.

I T seems silly now to be writing to you both, Brenda read. But I'd made up my mind and there's so much I have to thank you for and I know there won't be time tomorrow.

"You were right." Martin nodded, but Brenda ignored him, her eyes scanning the paper as she continued to read.

My room looks strange, too tidy, I suppose. I've cleared out all my old things, and lifted my wedding dress outside the wardrobe to let any creases drop out – and to look at it, of course.

Perhaps that's what made me want to write this letter, Mum and Dad. I feel so happy and I want you to be happy, too. I never wanted to hurt you. I've wanted to try to tell you over these last weeks, but there have been too many words, haven't there? I'm sorry for the harsh ones I used.

Again Martin's hand found Brenda's. Yes, there had been too much said, Chris was right. He wished he could take some of it back. They'd all said things which they didn't really mean.

But I want you to understand, the letter continued. I have to marry

Patrick, because like I told you, Mum, I have to make my own life, the way you always taught me.

Brenda looked towards Martin. "She means how we always . . ." But Martin stopped her. "Just read it, love."

I want this more than I've ever wanted anything. Surely that can't be wrong? But I love you, too. We've had such a good life together, the three of us. I couldn't bear anything to spoil all those happy memories.

The fun we had together. The holidays when we went camping. I used to think it was always hot and sunny then, but now I can remember the rain. It didn't matter though, did it?

N O, it hadn't mattered. Brenda remembered those days in the tent. No matter what the weather they had dressed up and gone for long walks over the cliff-tops and come back glowing with health. Then there'd been delicious hot soup, and games of Monopoly which had got sillier and sillier as the hours passed.

And Christmas! Do you remember those times as I do? Sunday afternoons watching some old film on television and, Mum, you always cried, and Dad would tease you.

Of course there were bad times! Like the time there should have been the baby and you lost it, Mum. I know how that hurt you both. I was sorry too, but sorry for you, not myself. Secretly I was a little glad, because I didn't want to share you with anyone.

It seems strange to know I could feel like that then, and now I'm going to leave you. But you won't be sharing me with Patrick.

What I feel for him is different – but of course you'll both know that, loving each other as you do.

She's growing up, Brenda thought, if she can see that. And yet she doesn't fully understand what her going will mean to us. She leant over and kissed Martin gently on the cheek, then began to read again.

We did try not to be in love. We knew all the things Dad told me that day – but it was no use. Love isn't like having the measles, you can't get over it just by being sensible.

And Patrick was sensible, even if I wasn't. He warned me that I might be attracted to someone else when he seems older than me, someone nearer my own age.

Brenda's voice faltered but she swallowed hard and read on.

Lots of people do that and it has nothing to do with ages. We've got to take our chance like everyone else. But we did stay apart for some months, only it was no use. I just kept thinking about all the good things we had going for us. Like the way Patrick is more sensible than I am; that he hasn't my temper, and he knows how to deal with me when I get mad.

Our personalities seem to balance each other, and that's a good thing, wouldn't you say? And I was so miserable without him. Perhaps you remember that time when I wasn't fit to live with? You thought I was sickening for something, remember, Mum?

Yes, Brenda remembered. She'd wanted Chris to go to the doctor but that had only caused another row.

"I'm not a child!" Chris had stormed. "Don't treat me like one."

THIS letter certainly explained a lot of things, Brenda thought, as she read on.

So I came and said we wanted to get married. We knew you'd object, but there was no other way, not after the way you've brought me up. Patrick shares your high standards and wouldn't have wanted us to do anything else but get married. No modern ideas about living together for him. But that only makes me love him more.

You see, dear Mum and Dad, I only want what you have. You've shown me what marriage should be, and we feel it's the only way our love can flourish. When I see how happy you are, can you blame me for wanting the same?

Can you blame me for wanting to live my life with the man I love? I know it won't be easy, is it ever? You joke about it – about Dad wanting to pack up and leave, and about you offering to help him, but there's some truth in it, isn't there?

THE young monkey!" Martin chuckled. "Fancy throwing that up against us."

"But she's right, love. There were times when I'd cheerfully have walked out," Brenda reminded him.

"You didn't, though, did you?" His smile was tender.

"I don't think Chris will either," Brenda said thoughtfully.

So tomorrow, Dad, I'll put on the lovely dress you bought me, and I'll slip my arm through yours. I hope you'll feel you can smile at me like you always do when you know I'm nervous. I can almost hear you saying, as you've done many times before, "Let's get this show on the road." Then I'll be able to walk down the aisle looking serene and composed.

But when I pass the pew where you're standing, Mum, please look up at me. Give me that wink, that knowing look we've always shared when Dad was playing at being a stern father.

You see, all this has been your fault. If you hadn't brought me up to believe that love meant marriage, and marriage meant happiness, I might never have taken this step. I've always known that you love me, but there's always been that special love which only you two share, and I was on the outside.

Now I'm going to enter that circle with my darling Patrick. And remember, when the organ peals tomorrow and when I make my vows – you've only yourselves to blame.

There were some more words and a row of crosses, but Brenda couldn't read them because Martin was hugging and kissing her.

"She's all right! That girl of ours is all right!" His voice was loud as he laughed.

"Hush, Martin! Hush!" Brenda placed a hand over his mouth teasingly.

"I'm not shouting!" Martin protested, but he grinned. "Anyway, I've got something to shout about, haven't I?" □

A World Of Difference

by
Alice Mackie

SHEILA MURDOCH picked up the bread she had ordered at the baker's, then paused as the smell of freshly-baked cream cakes wafted past her. Mentally counting the last of her week's housekeeping, she looked at the cakes a second time and decided.

"Two meringues and two eclairs," she said.

Sheila hurried home with her purchases, glancing at the clock above the jeweller's window to see that she still had an hour to spare before her mother-in-law's bus was likely to arrive.

Mrs Dora Murdoch had sent her a brief note just two days ago to say she would be making a visit to see her and Alan on Friday, and hoped it would be convenient.

It certainly would be convenient, Sheila thought, because Lochside was a long way from Glasgow and Alan saw very little of his parents these days.

She and Alan had felt themselves very lucky to get a house and to be able to buy a few pieces of furniture and carpets, but there was no doubt that their taste had had to be governed by price rather than choice.

She admired Alan's parents very much and she especially admired their lovely home which had the most beautiful paintings and ornaments Sheila had ever seen.

"Everything is so lovely," she said to Mrs Murdoch, when Alan first took her home to meet his parents, "and so well chosen. Your home is beautiful, Mrs Murdoch."

"I'm sure yours will be too, Sheila," Alan's mother told her. "If you start by furnishing it with love, the rest will soon come."

S HE and Alan had certainly put love into their home, but very little else. Alan was not handy in the house, like his father, and anyway he sat most nights over his books studying for his Civil Service examinations.

Sheila had a part-time job in the local library, and although she cleaned regularly and the house was always tidy, they had no time or money for decoration. There was, however, a little time for Sheila to spend on their garden — which was surprisingly easy to keep.

Sheila sighed as she turned away from the shop window and boarded the bus for home. Mrs Murdoch had seemed very quiet during her last visit and she and Sheila had very little to say to one another.

That had only been a few short weeks ago and she had not expected to see her in-laws for a few months. Now Sheila was feeling a trifle concerned over what had brought the older woman to Lochside on this extra visit.

Could there be something wrong which Mrs Murdoch thought she had to tell her in person, instead of writing her usual letter?

Sheila bit her lip as she prepared tea for herself and her mother-in-law.

She had baked some cakes which could not match up to Mrs Murdoch's standards, but at least she had her delicious cream cakes. They brightened up the tea table enormously and Sheila began to look at the clock with anticipation.

It was really very nice to have this extra visit, whatever the reason for it.

M RS DORA MURDOCH was also thinking about Sheila and Alan as she sat in the comfortable coach which swung out of the bus station in Glasgow and into the stream of traffic.

There was a heavy bag on the seat beside her, and Mrs Murdoch looked at it doubtfully. Was she doing the right thing, she wondered.

She wished that the journey from Glasgow to Lochside was not quite so long and expensive, or she would have got to know her new daughter-in-law a great deal better, but the young couple had only known one another for a few months when they married, and even when the girl came to stay with them before the wedding there still hadn't been time to get to know her properly.

"Do you think I'm doing the right thing?" she had asked John, and received his usual answer.

"You know best, my dear. Don't ask me to fathom out the workings of a woman's mind."

"Oh . . . you!" she said in mock exasperation and threw a cushion at him.

"One woman excepted," he told her, tenderly, "and while we're on the subject, you look terrific."

"What are you after?" she asked, with a laugh.

It was funny how, over the years, Dora had not bothered too much about how she looked. Always her first thought had been for her home and her family, and every penny she had saved was spent on them.

She had good taste in home-making and gradually she had bought all the little extras which went to make a home charming and comfortable.

WHEN Alan had left home and gone to work in a Civil Service job at Lochside, Mrs Murdoch had been lonely for a short while, but when he wrote to tell her about Sheila, and the fact that he wanted to get married, she cheered up again. A wedding in the family would be lovely!

Mrs Murdoch decided to buy herself a new outfit, something she hadn't had for years.

Feeling very smart for once, Mrs Murdoch dressed for Alan and Sheila's wedding, and admired herself in the dressing-table mirror.

John had hired a dress suit, and looked very distinguished, and Mrs Murdoch was well satisfied with both of them. She thoroughly enjoyed the wedding, and got on extremely well with Sheila's parents. So all-in-all it was a great success.

At home again that night she sighed as she lovingly covered her precious suit, and hung it up. It would be brought out on special occasions, she decided, and in the meantime she had her old skirts and jumpers.

Mrs Murdoch was delighted that the young couple had managed to find a house and were being sensible about furnishing it. She and John had enjoyed building up their home over the years and she was glad that Sheila did not insist on having everything at once.

When she and John visited the young couple a few weeks after the wedding, she had started off enjoying herself very much. It was so nice to have another family to love, and one day there might even be grandchildren.

"We have a treat in store for you," Alan had said. "Haven't we, darling?"

"A surprise, I think," Sheila'd laughed. "My uncle took a film of our wedding and he has lent it to Alan to show you this evening. I've also got the wedding photos to show you."

A ND it was exciting. There was a great deal of laughter and admiration as the film showed Alan and his best man looking so elegant in morning dress, and Sheila looking breathtakingly lovely in her bridal gown.

Mrs Murdoch had been pleased that the girl had chosen a long white dress and pretty veil.

Then there was a flash of lime green, and suddenly it was Mrs Murdoch's turn. Her mouth fell open in astonishment and the slow hot colour began to mount her cheeks. She looked enormous!

She realised that she appeared quite normal to the other three. They looked at her all the time, but she rarely saw herself in a full-length mirror. At one time she had been as slender as Sheila, and now although she was only in her early fifties, she was fat and middle aged, and looked much older than John.

After tea Sheila turned the knife in the wound by bringing out her big album of wedding photographs. Mrs McNair, Sheila's mother, looked elegant in a pale lilac suit, but to balance the photograph, Mrs Murdoch had been placed at the other side of the photograph and her lime-green suit and hat seemed to dominate every photograph in which she had been placed. She was smiling happily, but she looked terrible.

The Living Room

C HAIRS pulled up to a cheery fire;
Curtains drawn against the night;
Brasses that hang on oaken beams,
And wink and glint in the fire's light.

Logs that crackle and spit in the grate;
Shadows dancing along the wall;
The steady sound of the grandfather
clock
That stands at the end of the
darkened hall.

Now, evenings of winter are fast
drawing in,
And lamps are lit early to banish
the gloom.
For though the wind rages round
chimney and roof
It's peaceful and snug in the living
room.

Sylvia Crossley.

"I . . . I don't think I've taken a very good photo," she said tentatively and there was immediate dissent.

"Oh, Mum, you look fine," Alan said, "better than I've seen you for years."

Mrs Murdoch said no more. She looked down at her shapeless skirt and sweater, and thought that if the lime green was so becoming, what must she look like ordinarily?

B ACK home, Mrs Murdoch had spent a quiet, thoughtful week taking stock of herself. She had a beautiful home, but there was no doubt in her mind that the one unattractive note in it was herself!

She thought about the organisation she had heard about which helped one to lose weight, and discovered that she could go there once a week. Then after re-thinking her eating habits, she might begin to regain the shapely figure she had disastrously lost.

She looked at John once or twice and wondered if she ought to confide in him, but after an attempt to tell him about her problem, she had given up.

"Er . . . do you think I look OK, dear?" she had asked him. "I mean, don't you think . . . well . . . I'm not quite the same as I used to be."

"Eh . . . what?" John had asked. "You look fine to me. You look the same as you always have."

He gave her a kiss and she smiled a little, thinking that at least she had John's love. He did not appear to notice how far she had let herself go.

At first she found her new diet hard to take, but after a little, as her weight dropped, she began to feel invigorated by her new appearance.

She looked at her old skirts and felt they would be no loss if they went to a jumble sale, and she found herself paying regular visits to a shop in town which she'd only glanced in before.

Gradually Mrs Murdoch began to build herself a new wardrobe, and even found the courage to look at herself in the new full-length mirror she'd bought. She also went back to her hairdresser and had her hair cut in a new style which was simple but elegant.

M RS MURDOCH had walked into the house one evening wearing her new skirt and coat, as John rose from his favourite chair to turn off the TV. Suddenly he was really looking at his wife for the first time in months.

"Dora! You look . . . you look different somehow. Is it your hair?"

"My hair and my figure, and my clothes. Haven't you noticed that I'm losing weight, John?"

He stared at her. She looked ten years younger.

"Why, Dora, you look . . . you look quite beautiful," he said slowly. "As a matter of fact I hadn't noticed, but now I do.

"Don't overdo it, dear, or you'll be swapping me next for some fine young fellow," he said, laughing. "I like my nice comfortable wife."

"You've still got her, John," she said, fondly. "I've learned that you needn't sacrifice comfort for appearance, but at least you can be proud of me now." This started her thinking along different lines.

"You know, it's not a bad idea to begin shedding things you don't really need at our time of life. In fact, I seem to have been acquiring far too much I don't need. Now I wonder if I ought to go and see Alan and Sheila . . ."

She began to talk about her plans for the young people while John listened carefully. There was no stopping her when she got an idea into her head. He'd never been able to talk her out of anything and with his new-look wife he was willing to let her have whatever she wanted. It was hard to believe she was his Dora.

Sheila, too, could hardly believe it was her mother-in-law when she eventually met her off the bus. She had been looking for a well-built woman in a dark raincoat with a pull-on hat, but it was a tallish lady in a delicately feminine dress who stepped from the bus, then turned to lift down a heavy bag.

"I . . . I've brought this along. Sheila," she said, feeling rather awkward. "I'll tell you about it when we get home. Well, how are you, my dear?"

"Fine," Sheila said, lamely.

She caught a whiff of sweet flowery perfume and she saw that Mrs Murdoch's shoes were of the very latest design. Her handbag was an exact match, and Sheila was suddenly conscious of her own rather faded summer dress. She certainly looked dowdy beside Mrs Murdoch!

S HE soon forgot her appearance, however, when they arrived home and the sun was shining brightly, showing the garden at its best. Sheila suggested they sit outside.

Settling herself at Mrs Murdoch's feet, she began to relate all the latest news.

They chattered on until the sky started to cloud over and, deciding it was time for tea, they retired indoors.

"I've made us heaps of sandwiches and scones," Sheila said, excitedly. "Oh, and we have gorgeous cream cakes."

Mrs Murdoch's mouth watered, but her willpower had grown as her inches had reduced.

"No cakes for me," she said, firmly, "but I'll enjoy a ham sandwich, dear. No sugar either. I've got some saccharines in my handbag."

"You've been dieting," Sheila said, almost accusingly.

"Yes," Mrs Murdoch agreed, "as a matter of fact, I . . . I decided to get rid of a few things — starting with my overweight pounds, my shapeless clothes and . . ." she looked hesitantly at Sheila, "my excess ornaments and small fancy bits of furniture.

"My dear, I hope you don't mind, but I've brought some of them here in this bag for you to choose what you'd like."

"I . . . I'm sorry you find the house so dull. I wondered if you had last time you were here."

Mrs Murdoch had been taking out some of her most precious possessions: pretty china ladies, slender animals and birds, and oval pictures of delicate flowers set in silver frames.

She paused, amazed. "You mean you thought I was quiet because I was looking at your bare walls? Oh, Sheila! I was quiet because of seeing myself in that film! At one time I was as slender as you, and I hadn't noticed my own figure piling on the inches, what with making my own clothes and never really looking at myself. But the film and your wedding photographs were like buckets of ice cold water. They really woke me up!

"Now I'm going to be more sensible — I'm not going to sit at home all day admiring my bric-a-brac. Look, dear, I've divided it between you and me, and you'll do me a big favour if you spread this lot out in your room. There are a few tables, too, and small chairs and stools. If only you could find a corner for them, perhaps Alan could hire a van and pick them up."

SHEILA'S eyes glowed when she saw that the ornaments included a special favourite of hers, one she had dusted lovingly when she helped Mrs Murdoch in the Glasgow home.

"I . . . I can't believe it," she said. "Are you sure?"

"I'm very sure, and I hope they will give you and Alan pleasure. As for John and me, we're going to go out a little more and enjoy ourselves — in fact, we're going to join some clubs. You'll see us more often, too." She stopped and sighed. It was obvious she was looking forward to this change of habit.

"We were getting old before our time, wasting precious time caring for possessions. Life is so good these days, and the house much easier to manage."

"You look lovely," Sheila said. "Just wait till Alan sees you!"

Mrs Murdoch travelled home with her son's astonishment and admiration to hug to her heart.

After she had gone, Sheila made a fresh pot of tea for Alan and herself, and brought out her precious plate of creamy cakes. Her hand paused then hovered over them, then she drew back and caught sight of herself in the sideboard mirror.

Looking at herself with a new awareness she thought that she was looking rather more bulky and heavy than usual. In fact . . . She thought again about Mrs Murdoch's smart new looks.

"I think I'll have an apple, Alan," she said, looking at his thin, rangy figure. "Would you like a nice cream cake?" □

The Newest Arrival

By Margaret Nicol

THE red single-decker bus slowed down at a quiet crossroads and stopped with a screech of brakes.

"Miller's Farm!" called the conductress, and a slim, fair-haired girl took her suitcase down from the rack and stepped off the bus on to the deserted country road.

Looking round her as the bus moved away, Lois Boyd glimpsed a farm in the distance and closer at hand a stretch of wooded pasture. Quite near, she could see a caravan in a field, and made towards it, sure that it must be the caravan her sister, Tracey, had rented for the month.

Very nice, Lois thought, as she followed the grassy path. Just the very spot for her two small nieces, Fiona and Karen, to find freedom from the restrictions of town life. Tracey, too, with the birth of her third child so near, would be able to relax.

"Do you think it's wise to go on holiday just now?" Lois had asked her sister when she'd heard of the plan.

Tracey had merely laughed — she wasn't the worrying kind.

"I've got heaps of time to go before the baby comes. Why not?" she demanded. "With Rod on his travels for the firm, I'd be bored at home." She'd looked over at the two little girls. "Besides, it's the last holiday the wee ones might have for a long time.

"You'll come too, Lois, for a week or two, won't you?" Her glance had been appealing. "It would help me out."

Such an appeal for help wasn't to be ignored. Tracey was a happy-go-lucky person who tended to be rather vague about details, usually content to let things take their course. Though she loved her sister dearly, Lois had to admit there were times when she certainly needed to be "helped out."

So Lois had arranged to join them for the end of their stay, thinking it would be a chance to get to know her nieces better. Children grew up so quickly!

She had almost reached the caravan now. It was neat and modern with windows all round, but the curtains were drawn close, which wasn't like Tracey at all — and there was no sign of the children . . .

K NOCKING at the firmly-closed door, Lois waited expectantly. But there was no sound, no movement.

"Hi, there!" She knocked more loudly this time. "Is anybody at home?"

Then she stepped back as the door suddenly opened. But instead of Tracey, it was a man who stood there — a youngish, angry-looking man, with a frown on his face.

"I'm sorry." Lois smiled tentatively. "I thought this was my sister's caravan. Can you tell me, please, where it is?"

"There's another caravan over there." He pointed to a clump of trees. "Probably that's the one you want," he said abruptly.

The door closed, but not before Lois got a peep inside. The main thing that caught her eye was an uncovered typewriter on a table.

Oh dear, she had disturbed him at work.

She walked over to the trees he had indicated and came upon the other caravan, half hidden behind them. This one was larger, with a veranda, and the curtains were wide open. So was the door.

In fact, her two nieces had burst out and were on their way to meet her, Fiona leading the way.

She was a thin, shy, six-year-old with a charming smile, in spite of two missing front teeth. Plump little Karen, who was only two and a half and not in the least shy, trotted along behind her sister.

"Hello, darlings!" Lois put down her case and held out her arms. While Fiona held back, Karen rushed into them, returning her kisses fervently, till her sister pushed her away.

"Kiss me, too!" she demanded, and Lois laughingly did as she was told.

Tracey was on her way now, light footed in spite of her advanced state of pregnancy. She wore a loose blue frock and there was a happy smile on her face as she, too, hugged her sister.

"So you made it!" She laughed. "I'm glad you found us OK."

"Not at first," Lois told her. "I called at another caravan over there, but the man wasn't very pleased. He was busy typing, I think."

"Oh yes, that would be Ernest Page," she explained. "We don't have much to do with him. In fact, since Karen broke his window when she was playing with a ball, he just glowers at us. Quite obviously he doesn't like children!" Tracey made a face.

Lois decided there and then that while she was there she would avoid Mr Page as much as possible. It was a pity that, apart from the farm up the road, there were no other neighbours.

FOLLOWING Tracey into the caravan, she found it surprisingly roomy.

"We've got two bedrooms, and a bed-settee in the lounge for you," her sister explained as she showed Lois round. "Will it do?"

"That'll suit me fine." Lois promptly sat down. "It's quite luxurious, isn't it?" She looked round the caravan approvingly. "What a bright place."

"Oh, yes." Tracey nodded. "It has all mod. cons. — electricity and water laid on, a bathroom with a tiny bath, a fridge, and heaps of cupboards."

"What do you do when it rains?" Lois wanted to know.

"It hasn't dared to rain since we came." Tracey smiled happily. "We've been lucky, because the girls have been able to play in the field."

In the field at the back of the caravan there was a swing hanging from a stout branch of an apple tree.

Karen took Lois's hand and led her to it then she climbed on to the seat and demanded a "wee push" from her aunt.

"It's my turn now!" Fiona announced jealously.

"That's you busy till teatime." Tracey grinned.

True enough, there was no respite. Lois let her gaze wander now and again to the other caravan.

Only once was there a sign of life when Mr Page appeared for a moment, looked in the direction of the happy childish voices and, seemingly disgusted, shut his door again.

When the children were safely in bed and the light was growing dim, the two girls settled down for a sisterly chat.

DON'T you get lonely?" Lois looked over at Tracey as they enjoyed a cup of coffee.

"With these two live wires around?" she asked. "Not me. When I need adult company I go up to the farm. Mrs Dow always has plenty of news.

"They own these two caravans and let them by the month. I get the lowdown on the characters of the former occupants — Mr Page's, too. He left his wife, I gather, to write a book or something like that."

"Oh, he's that sort of man," Lois remarked. "No wonder he didn't look very pleased to see me!

"What kind of book is he writing?" she asked Tracey. "Not a romantic one, surely."

"Ask Mrs Dow, she'll tell you," Tracey answered.

"I don't think I'm interested enough! As for him leaving his wife — why should he do such a thing?" she demanded.

"Don't ask me." Tracey laughed. "Why *do* men run away from wives? Perhaps she nagged him . . ."

Suddenly quiet, she dragged herself up from her chair.

"I think I'll go to bed, now, I'm feeling rather tired. I hope you sleep well, Lois."

"You, too." Lois eyed her sister anxiously. "Are you sure you're feeling all right, Tracey?" she asked solicitously.

"Of course I'm all right. I just wish it was all over — we're hoping for a boy this time!"

Lois kissed her sister goodnight, then got ready for bed herself. The settee bed was comfortable and in no time at all she was fast asleep.

H OW long it was before she woke to the patter of rain on the roof she couldn't tell, it was still dark in the caravan.

Moving a curtain, she saw a rain-splashed window and trees waving wildly against an inky sky. The caravan itself was giving little shudders as the wind whirled round it. She hoped it wouldn't wake the children.

Suddenly, there was another sound, and Tracey was there beside her, clutching her dressing-gown round her.

"Lois!" she gasped. "You'll have to help me. This baby is beginning to get a move on!"

"Tracey, get back to bed." Lois was on her feet in seconds. "Just tell me what to do . . ."

"You'd better ring for a doctor. There's a phone at the farm." Tracey's voice was tremulous.

"Right." Lois put an arm round her sister. "Try to keep calm, dear. You're going to be all right!"

She hurriedly threw on some clothes, seized a pair of wellingtons, then opened the door. A swirl of wind and rain blew in, almost winding her as she staggered out on to the slippery, wet grass, groping her way in the dark.

The only thing to be seen was the light in Mr Page's caravan. There was nothing else for it. Any port in a storm, she decided, as she stumbled towards it.

He came at her second knock, looming very large in the narrow doorway. The light of the torch he shone upon Lois made her blink.

"Is something wrong?" he demanded.

"I'm sorry to disturb you, but there's a crisis. My sister . . ."

"I see," he broke in before she could go on. "She's having her baby. You'll want to phone the doctor!" It was a statement of fact, rather than a question.

So he was human, after all.

"Yes, I don't think I should leave her, and I'll never get to the farm in this storm!"

"Would you like me to go for you?" His smile, so unexpected, gave her courage. "Of course I'll go, just give me a moment to get ready."

He emerged in a big yellow mac, very decisive and matter-of-fact.

"Take my arm," he ordered and led Lois back to Tracey's caravan. "Now, stay there till I get back, and tell your sister not to panic. They give good service here."

He disappeared into the dark, the light from his torch pinpointing his progress.

IT'S OK, Mr Page has things in hand," Lois comforted Tracey, who was on her feet clumsily packing things into a case, lips firmly pressed together. "Are the girls all right?"

A peep into their little room revealed two angelic figures, sound asleep.

Karen's fair curls were tossed round her baby face and Fiona's dark head was buried in her pillow.

"Let's hope they stay like that," Lois said with relief in her voice.

Fortunately they did sleep on, even when the doctor came and shortly after his visit, the ambulance. They carried out their duties very quietly and efficiently.

"We'll contact the farm when there's something to report," Lois was told. "If you're anxious, you can phone the hospital, but your sister seems perfectly all right."

"Kiss the wee ones for me." Tracey's last words before she left were rueful. "I'm sorry to let you in for this, Lois. I must have miscalculated — you know what a featherbrain I am!"

LOIS tried to go back to sleep, but it was useless. She lay listening to the unaccustomed sounds round the caravan. The wind had fallen and there was no more patter of rain. She could hear the faint twittering of a dawn chorus, the lowing of cattle and the rattle of a passing vehicle on the road.

"Mummy! Tell Karen to get out of my bed!" a small voice called from the girls' room.

She was beside them in a moment. Karen was bounding up and down on top of her protesting sister. Lois caught her up in her arms.

"I want Mummy!" Fiona demanded. "Where is she?"

Lois decided to tell them the truth.

"She's gone to hospital for a wee while," she explained. "We'll go in and see her tomorrow, perhaps."

"Oh yes, she told us. She's gone to get the baby, hasn't she?"

"That's right, and she left me to look after you, so you'll have to show me where to find things, Fiona."

They were having breakfast when they heard footsteps on the veranda. Ernest Page grinned through the window at them. He looked much younger today, almost boyish, in a T-shirt and jeans.

When Lois opened the door to him, he held up two bottles of milk, smiling broadly. He wasn't a brusque stranger any longer, Lois realised, but a friend to whom she felt really grateful.

"I've just been up at the farm," he told her. "They gave me your milk, and a piece of good news. The hospital phoned to say that your sister had a little boy, and everything's fine."

Lois felt a wave of relief as his words sank in.

"Have we got a baby brother?" Fiona wanted to make sure she had heard right.

"Yes, darlings, isn't that super?" Lois hugged them both tightly, then turned to Ernest, who was watching the little scene with laughing eyes.

"I'll have to let their father know," she told him. "Perhaps the farm will let me phone Hugh."

They all went up to the farm together and Ernest introduced her to the farmer's wife, who was kindness itself. Getting through to Hugh's office,

Worthy Of Note

Ｈ OW grand to hear a choirboy's
voice,
No lark upon the wing
Could such melodious music make
Nor greater pleasure bring.

A loving mother's lullaby
Falls gently on the ears,
To be recalled with tender thoughts
Throughout our later years.

And when love seeks us out
Is there not always one sweet song
That soon becomes our very own
And helps our love along?

A melody may cheer and charm
As nothing else can do.
For music is a special joy
That lasts our whole life through.

Irene Bernaerts.

Lois was told that they would do their best to locate him and give him the news.

"Lucky chap," Ernest remarked as they made their way back to the caravan. "Two lovely little daughters — and now a baby boy."

"I got the impression you didn't like children." Lois smiled.

Ernest reddened through his tan.

"It's not true, believe me," he retorted. "I know I was a bit grumpy when the wee one broke my window, but it happened at a bad time." He held out a hand to Karen and the child slipped her small one into it trustingly. "See? She forgives me, don't you, pet?"

"Yes, please," the wee girl smiled up at him.

"So you do know a little about children," Lois commented "Have you any of your own?"

It had seemed a perfectly natural question to ask, yet Ernest looked puzzled.

"Me?" His eyebrows rose. "I'm not married — would I be here alone if I were?"

"I must have misunderstood when my sister told me the only other person near at hand was a man who was living away from his wife. Mrs Dow had mentioned it to her . . ." Lois felt herself blushing in confusion.

Ernest looked at her blankly, then he started to laugh.

"Your sister certainly did get it wrong! It was my predecessor in the caravan who did that."

"I see . . ." Inexplicably, Lois felt her spirits soar. "That's just like Tracey, she gets everything confused!

"I suppose that story about your writing a book is mixed up, too," she went on, picking her way carefully down the stony path, keeping a watchful eye on Fiona and Karen.

"Well, not quite. I'm doing a history of my dad's firm — it's a hundred years since it was founded," Ernest explained. "They make tiny models of soldiers and that kind of thing. I work there myself, but the writing bit goes against the grain . . ." He broke off to catch Lois's arm. "Careful there! This path is treacherous."

When Lois recovered her balance, she returned to the subject of writing. "So that was why you glowered at me yesterday when I called at your caravan by mistake," she declared.

"Did I glower?" he asked innocently. "I'm so sorry." He smiled down at her. "You weren't the cause, then, it was my old typewriter that wouldn't work. Do you happen to know anything about type-writers?"

"Just what I've picked up in the office." Lois shrugged her shoulders. "But I'll have a look at yours sometime, if you like."

"That's great!" He sounded pleased. "If you do that, I'll help you to look after these mischievous nieces of yours."

JUST then there was a wail from Karen, who had tripped over a stone. Lois knelt down and put her arms round the sobbing toddler.

"All right, pet," she consoled the wee girl. "Show me where it hurts."

Still upset, Karen pointed to the graze on her knee.

"I want Mummy to come and kiss it better!" she wailed.

"Won't I do? I've got kisses, too." She picked Karen up and cuddled her close to her, kissing her lovingly.

Ernest Page looked on in appreciation, as with the tears still wet on her cheeks, Karen's face broke into smiles. It was like the sun coming out after rain.

"Better now!" she said, and trotted off happily after Fiona.

"You managed that very well," Ernest said admiringly, looking at Lois in a way that brought a becoming blush to her cheeks. "Second nature to you, I guess."

During the following week while Tracey was away, Ernest was as good as his word. Without his help, Lois would have been harassed coping with everything — the caravan, the cooking, and the children.

His small car was invaluable when it came to shopping in the village, and visiting Tracey in hospital.

The little girls loved playing the games he invented for them, making playthings out of everyday, simple objects.

"Simple, but effective," he would say to Lois. "I like simple things, don't you?"

Lois agreed with him. In fact, they seemed to agree about almost everything. She'd never met anyone whose views fitted in with her own so well.

THE day came when Tracey's husband appeared to take his wife and family home in his big car.

Lois had volunteered to stay on till the next day to tidy the caravan and settle up with Mrs Dow at the farm.

She waved them goodbye from the roadside. Tracey and Hugh, the two little girls and the new baby — Nicholas, they were going to call him. Fiona already loved him; Karen hadn't quite made up her mind about having a little brother.

"She's not the baby any longer, you see," Lois pointed out to Ernest, who was standing there by her side, a place where he seemed to enjoy being . . .

The car turned a bend in the road then was lost to sight, and the two of them silently made their way back to the now-deserted caravan. They didn't speak till they reached the door.

"You're free now to get on with your typing," Lois remarked, trying to sound bright and cheerful. "I'm very grateful to you for all you've done."

"Have you forgotten that my typewriter is out of order?" He smiled into her eyes. "Or that you promised to have a look at it? I can't possibly get on till you do that — and there's no time like the present, is there?"

"Oh, but . . ." she began to protest. "I've got such heaps of things to do before I leave."

Ernest tucked her hand firmly in his, and when he spoke his voice was tender.

"All that can wait," he declared masterfully. "Come with me." And he propelled her over to his caravan.

The typewriter was still sitting there on the table and Lois walked over to have a look at it. But she had barely touched the keys when Ernest placed his hand gently over hers.

"Leave it," he told her. "We've only got a day, and time is precious. If your tidying-up can wait, so can my typing!" He drew her close to him.

"Up till now we've been looking after other people, but now we can think of ourselves. Say you agree that we should spend every single minute together . . ."

Lois felt safe and happy in his arms.

"Together," she murmured, revelling in the warmth of his embrace.

"Together forever," he corrected her, kissing her tenderly. □

It's Not The Same, Any More

S HE seemed to have done nothing but go to parties since she came home. Sociable as she was, Anna Montgomery was weary of the constant flow of visitors and their pressing invitations to Michael and herself to pay return calls.

Her husband, on the other hand, appeared to welcome all the attention they were receiving.

"Surely it's natural that folk want to see you after all these months away," he reasoned.

Anna bit her lip, aware there was no reproach in his tone, though somehow she would have felt more at ease if there had been. It wasn't her fault that her six-week trip to San Francisco after her brother-in-law's unexpected death had stretched to six months. There had been a variety of reasons, the main one being that her sister's health had suffered with the shock of bereavement.

It had been a wrench leaving Michael for so long, but his letters had proved a comfort during that difficult time. He had worried that Anna might be taking on too much with the work involved in nursing her sister as well as cooking and cleaning for her niece and nephew.

He had made no complaint when the return trip had to be postponed again but Anna had sensed his disappointment. Luckily his job was a demanding one and the firm dealing in ceramics was expanding all the time.

Most of his meals had been eaten out during her absence — something she had vowed would be changed now she was home again.

This morning she was up early, as usual, and already the delicious aroma of bacon and eggs was wafting its way up to the bedroom.

"Five minutes and it'll be on the table, Michael," she called. "Don't let it get cold."

W HEN he arrived a few minutes later, he kissed his wife affectionately. "The weather seems to have changed at last," he said.

"Mm, it's a beautiful day." Then they ate in silence, but that at least was nothing new, she reassured herself.

Since coming home, so many things seemed to have changed; it was consoling to find that one thing at least was as it had always been.

He's thinner, Anna thought with a pang — or had she just remembered him more filled out? She was sure there were extra lines in his face, but then his job carried a lot of responsibility.

"What are your plans for today, love?" Michael asked, aware of her scrutiny.

by Ruth Sinclair

"Oh, shopping for Robin and Meg's supper this evening — and ours, of course," she answered his question. "What time do you expect to be home, Michael?"

He was frowning.

"Did I mention there was a meeting with the Belgians today?" he asked. When she shook her head, he lowered his eyes and continued.

"We usually end up by wining and dining them. I'm afraid I won't want much to eat when I get in. I should be back before Robin and Meg leave, but knowing them I'm sure they won't mind."

"If I'd known earlier, I could have put them off until another night," she said, a trace of annoyance in her voice.

Although she was fond of Michael's brother and his wife, she was in no mood to entertain them on her own, not with this cloud of uncertainty enveloping her.

O RIGINALLY the intention had been to stay in the States only as long as it would take Tricia to get over the initial shock of losing her husband. Then as Christmas drew nearer Anna couldn't bear the thought of leaving the two small children and their newly-widowed mother on their own. She knew this would be the time when they would feel their loss the most.

So Anna had written to Michael asking if he could possibly come over to spend Christmas in San Francisco. At first he had thought it might just be possible.

But if not, then I'm all for you staying to help Tricia and the young-sters over their difficult time. Of course I'll miss you, but things are pretty hectic here right now and I don't see me having much time to sit and brood at home in an empty house.

So please don't worry your head about me – I'll get by. As I say, if I can possibly manage away I'll fly over, depend upon it, he had written.

The next letter brought news of the Belgians who were anxious to link up with production in Antwerp. Unfortunately the only time a mutually convenient meeting could be arranged was the twenty-first of December. Of course, that put paid to Michael's intention to join them for Christmas.

Still, Anna consoled herself, it wouldn't be too long till she herself was booked on the flight home in early January. All it meant was that their celebrations would be a little later than usual — and would be all the sweeter when the time came.

A NNA had been full of admiration for her sister's courage and determination to let nothing spoil the children's Christmas, even giving a party for their friends. Then only three days before Anna was due to fly home, her sister fell victim to flu and once more Anna had to take over the running of the home. Her reunion with her husband was delayed yet again.

Michael was sympathetic, but his letters were becoming scrappier than ever — not that he had ever been especially fluent when it came to letter-writing.

I'm longing to see you again, Michael darling, she wrote. *I do hope you've been taking care of yourself and not working too hard. Roll on the day when I can make it all up to you. You've been such a dear throughout – no impatience, no reproaches.*

The day came at last when she could take her leave of Tricia and the children with an easy mind, after wringing a promise from them that they would come over to Scotland just as soon as they could.

"It would put you on your feet again," Anna had coaxed her sister. "Think how nice it would be to come home again."

But Tricia had shaken her dark head.

"This is my home now," she'd said softly. "And I wouldn't want to live anywhere else. I've made marvellous friends here and my neighbours couldn't have been kinder. Still, I would like to see the old country once again so that the children would see where our roots were. Yes, we'll be over sometime, Anna."

"Meantime, safe journey, love. I'm not even going to try to thank you for all you've done for me and the children. I just don't know how we'd have managed without you."

Still basking in the warmth of her sister's gratitude, Anna settled herself into a window seat in the huge plane. She was glad she'd been some help to Tricia. It was too painful to imagine how she would have felt if it had been Michael who'd died, but when it did enter her mind it was terrifying.

Tricia had been very brave and Anna couldn't help admiring her courage.

WHEN the plane touched down and she glimpsed Michael waiting for her behind the barrier at the terminal, every thought fled except the feeling of how wonderful it was to be home again, safe in his arms.

"Welcome back, love," he said, hugging her warmly.

The lump in her throat made it difficult to answer him, so she merely clung to him tightly.

"I've missed you so much, Michael!" she answered, when eventually she was able to speak. "I'd never have believed six months could be so long."

Once in the car speeding homewards, Anna kept up a flow of cheerful chatter till it dawned on her that it was proving a somewhat one-sided conversation.

"Michael, how have you been?" Her concern expressed itself in the warm tone of her voice.

"You've picked up the American way of talking," he remarked. "Still, I like it."

It was only later it struck Anna he had been unusually silent during the run home, though every now and again he had smiled or nodded agreement to something she had been saying.

But he was thinner, there was no mistake about that, and preoccupied, too, she thought. That job was taking too much out of him. She knew it was the old story of the willing horse getting most of the work to do.

The garden had been tended and there were flowers in the sitting-room as well as the entrance hall. Michael seemed a bit embarrassed when she thanked him warmly.

"Oh, I can't take the credit for it," he told her quickly. "I got the professionals to come in and make a good job of it."

"Well, it's gorgeous, and it was nice of you to bother, Michael." Impulsively Anna kissed her husband, but just then the phone rang and he hurried off to answer it. A few moments later, she heard his voice raised in anger.

"Look, I arranged to have the day off!" he remonstrated. "This morning, at the very least, to welcome my wife back from the States. Surely there's someone in Bradley's who can handle decisions in my absence . . . ?"

He was still fuming when he came back to drink the coffee Anna had prepared.

"I really don't mind being left on my own," she assured him. "In fact, I can use the time to unpack and settle in again. Please don't worry if you have to go in to the office after all, Michael."

"Well I suppose I'd better go in and sort out the problem," Michael decided. "Oh, by the way, the neighbours have asked if we'll go in this evening. They wanted to give you a welcome-home party."

"Lovely! Which neighbours — just so I don't go to the wrong house?" She laughed.

"It's the MacCallums tonight," he informed her. "The Denvers have claimed tomorrow, so be prepared!"

Anna enjoyed the attention and the kindly gestures from the neighbours on either side, but when the same thing happened each evening it began to pall, especially when everyone kept asking Anna the same question — would she like to live permanently in the United States?

"I might," was her response, "but only if Michael was there, too."

Maybe it was Anna's imagination, but Celia Lindsay, whose husband was one of Bradley's managers, had given her a strange look when she'd heard this answer. There was no opportunity, however, to find out the reason, but the more Anna thought of that enigmatic look the more convinced she became that the woman, for some reason, was pitying her.

THIS morning, as luck would have it, Anna arrived at the hair-dresser's to find Celia Lindsay sitting under a drier. Temporarily deafened by the noise of the blower, the other woman had shouted across the shampoo-room.

"If you're not doing anything, we could have lunch together. What do you say, Anna?"

She'd never particularly liked Celia, but out of politeness — and still remembering her strange look — Anna simply nodded agreement.

Moments later, her hair was being shampooed and set by a young assistant, which Anna usually enjoyed. If only Celia's face hadn't been in the background, reflected in the mirror above the basin!

I'm going to find out what's on that woman's mind, she vowed, even if I have to sit through a lunch I don't particularly want. She had experienced samples of Celia's acid tongue in the past, usually commenting against some unsuspecting "friend."

Anna wasn't one to gossip and usually gave Celia a wide berth, but there were times when her remarks could be helpful.

"I want to hear all about your trip, you lucky thing," Celia Lindsay gushed, when they were at last free of the hairdresser's and on their way to a suitable restaurant.

YOU'RE looking well," Celia declared, as they waited for their first course to arrive. "No wonder, after that marvellous holiday. Aren't you the lucky one — six months all on your own!"

It was hardly a holiday, Anna felt like pointing out as she recalled the nursing, cooking and cleaning on top of worrying about her sister. Still, what this woman thought didn't really matter. So instead she simply nodded.

"Yes, I did enjoy it. It was quite an experience."

"As I said, you were lucky, not many husbands would be willing to let their wives go off for so long, but then, of course . . ." Celia paused. "There I go chattering on, as usual. Tell me how you're liking being home again, Anna."

"Please finish what you were going to say." Of old, Anna knew Celia's tactics, and was half annoyed with herself for falling into the trap.

But Celia refused to be drawn, or at least not at that precise moment.

"Quite a few of Bradley's managerial staff dine in here, Anna," the other woman commented.

"Do they?" Anna replied. "What's wrong with the canteen then?"

"Maybe they like a change, or maybe it causes less talk if they pair off in a public restaurant, rather than in full view of the rest of the staff."

Anna felt a tiny shiver of apprehension. It was obvious Celia was leading up to something. But before anything more could be said the woman's attention was distracted by someone entering the restaurant.

Turning, Anna found herself looking at a very attractive young woman. She was a pretty girl with long, shiny, auburn hair, and the clothes she wore were simple but stylish.

The girl glanced across at the two women and Celia nodded, a small smile on her lips. The girl returned the nod and made her way to a table.

"What a beautiful girl! Is she a friend?" Anna inquired.

"No." Celia's tone was quite firm and Anna had the distinct impression she was mentally adding, I'm glad to say. "She's one of Bradley's managers — a newcomer. Hasn't Michael mentioned her?"

That knowing look was on Celia's face again and Anna, normally so placid and gentle, felt almost like hitting her. There was no mistaking what the look meant — if he hasn't mentioned her, he jolly well ought to have.

"Perhaps he has," she returned coolly, transferring her attention to the excellent meal. "I don't know her name, of course."

"Sandra Hollingwood, and she's in charge of design. Apparently she has an arts degree. But no doubt you'll be meeting her at the dance. You are going, aren't you?" Celia was anxious to know.

So far, Anna hadn't heard anything about the firm's annual dance, though she had gone with Michael to some of them in the past.

However, not for worlds would she have let Celia know that Michael hadn't mentioned the dance yet.

"I expect so," she answered, studying the dessert menu.

On the way out, Anna stole another look at the beautiful redhead in the far corner, still dining alone.

Celia's words echoed through her head.

"Not many husbands would be willing to let their wives go off for so long, but, then, of course . . ."

What had she been going to say?

She said a quick goodbye to Celia before she was tempted to ask her outright.

R OBIN and Meg were easy people to entertain and were not in the least put out by Michael's absence.

"That brother of mine is a glutton for work," Robin declared, turning the TV to a station Anna and his wife had requested.

"You wouldn't catch me working overtime — unless, of course, I'm being paid for it," he declared.

Michael arrived when they were halfway through the next programme and Anna hurried off to see to supper.

She'd enjoyed Robin and Meg's company, but throughout the evening the conversation between Celia and herself kept returning to her. It was the sort of nagging doubt that no matter how hard she tried to dispel it, it would reappear, only to have grown.

Michael rose to help, as she pushed the trolley through to the sitting-room.

"Had a good day, love?" he asked, pleasantly.

"It was interesting — hairdresser in the morning and lunch with Celia Lindsay." Then before she realised it, the words were out. "Oh, by the way, we saw Sandra Hollingwood in the restaurant." Out of the corner of her eye, she saw Robin and his wife exchange quick glances, and with a sick feeling inside her noticed Michael's face had reddened. She'd been so sure Celia had only been making trouble, but now the doubts were real, not just in her imagination.

"Oh yes?" Michael's voice was casual. "She's in charge of our patterns."

"Celia told me." Anna kept her voice light. "A designing woman . . ." The brittle joke fell flat as no-one laughed.

The tea and sandwiches tasted like ashes in Anna's mouth, but Michael wasn't easily embarrassed, he had recovered quickly. But she'd told herself she really had no need to probe any further — that tell-tale flush had told its own story. Michael had fallen in love with another woman!

She knew what Celia had been going to say, now.

"Not many husbands would be willing to let their wives go away for so long – only those who had someone else to keep them company!"

"Don't jump to conclusions," Meg whispered, as they washed up the supper dishes together.

"Why not — other people have," Anna said sharply, and told Meg about lunch-time.

"Don't let that woman influence you. You know Michael — she doesn't. You're right for each other and no-one else matters." There was no doubting Meg's sincerity.

"But I knew something was wrong when I got home, Meg," she said.

"Please don't be hasty," Meg said, softly. "It may not be as bad as you think."

THERE was silence after they had gone, and Anna pretended to busy herself tidying ashtrays.

"Well," Michael said, in a resigned voice. "I know there's something you want to say, so let's have it."

"All right," she said. "Tell me about Sandra Hollingwood . . ."

Michael didn't hesitate as he replied:

"She's twenty-nine, quite beautiful, intelligent, and now an important member of the staff." She waited expectantly for him to continue.

"And she isn't a designing woman, far from it," he added, with a quick reference to Anna's impulsive comment about the other woman.

"I'm sorry if what I said offended your good taste," she said ironically. "And even sorrier if I've aroused your protective instinct towards her. You seem to know her very well."

"Our work has thrown us together quite a bit," he admitted, avoiding her eyes.

"You've fallen in love with her?" It was more a statement of fact than a question.

"A little, perhaps." His voice was level.

The frank admission rocked Anna and she took a deep breath before plunging on — she had to know more. Looking down at her hands, she chose her words carefully.

"Thanks for being honest, Michael. What I want to know is where I stand in all this?" She had to force the words out. "Do you want to be free?"

"For goodness' sake, woman, what kind of question is that?" he demanded. "We're married. *Till death us do part,* remember?"

"What do you expect me to say?" She could feel her control slipping. "How could I live with you, knowing you wanted someone else?" Tears were threatening to spill, so Anna turned her face away from him.

"So you'd rather we split up, is that it?" His voice was harsh with anger.

Of course that wasn't what she wanted, and she turned to tell him that, but he'd left the room.

Stunned, she gazed into the fire and its dying embers, as his footsteps receded upstairs to the bedroom.

HOW long she sat there she couldn't tell, but faintly she became aware of the sound of Michael's footsteps coming downstairs and then into the kitchenette. There was the sound of water rushing and a kettle being filled.

How can he think of food at a time like this, she asked herself angrily.

When he eventually came into the sitting-room, he was carrying a tray with two steaming-hot drinks and he had prepared two awkwardly-cut sandwiches.

She stared from him to the offered tray, the inelegant mugs and the door-stop sandwiches, and suddenly her whole body was shaking with an almost hysterical, though silent, laughter. He sat down by her side and put an arm round her shoulders, holding her till she was in control of her emotions again.

"Just let me explain," he murmured tenderly. "Most of the men in the office are a little in love with Sandra — in fact, any warm-blooded male would be. But as far as I'm concerned she's just a nice girl. You're the one I chose — and I've never regretted it."

After a long moment he spoke again.

"Anyway, Sandra's a kind, very decent girl who isn't interested in happily-married men . . ."

"All right, all right — we've talked enough about Sandra," Anna broke in with a laugh. "But don't think I'm finished with you yet, Michael. Why haven't I been invited to the firm's dance?"

He kissed her lightly and grinned.

"I was planning to give us a holiday from it, this year, love. I know you don't enjoy it much," he answered simply.

"Oh, but this year I will." She giggled.

Perhaps she wouldn't like Sandra Hollingwood, she thought, and maybe Sandra wouldn't like her, but Anna was sure of one thing — now that Michael and she were completely together again, she knew one person who would be very perturbed to see Michael, Sandra and herself enjoying a friendly little chat at the dance — and that person was Celia Lindsay.

She looked into her husband's eyes, seeing reflected there the love and happiness she herself felt for him. But as he bent to kiss her Anna fleetingly pictured Celia's shocked face, staring disbelievingly at the three of them.

If she hadn't been otherwise occupied, she would have laughed and laughed. □

Tarbert stands at the head of Loch Tarbert and separates that sea-loch from the other sea arm, Loch Fyne. The once-prosperous herring port is situated at the north end of the now-famous Mull of Kintyre. The herring fishing industry has declined now, but yacht and boat building remains by this sheltered anchorage. Ruined Tarbert Castle overlooks the village and was once a stronghold of Robert the Bruce.

TARBERT LOCHFYNE : J CAMPBELL KERR

F

Week-End Of Decision

BY CLARE GIBBON

E ARLY morning sunlight filtered through the avenue of tall trees with all the promise of another glorious day. The grass was still damp with dew and refreshingly cool under Helen's bare feet. Entering the quiet woods, she breathed deeply and felt almost intoxicated with the old familiar scents of ferns and bracken.

There was no sound but bird-song and she stood quite still for a moment, listening and wondering at the peace of it all.

She had completely forgotten what she was wearing when she'd found herself heading for the woods after her long night's vigil. But instinctively she had known that this was the place where at least she could be alone, with space to breathe and time to think.

Reflecting upon what seemed the longest night in her life, it was hardly credible that it was barely 24 hours since she'd arrived back at her home in Crompton.

The north-bound breakfast train had been crowded and she'd been lucky to get a seat. Before long, Helen had turned from scrutinising her fellow passengers and had become engrossed in the paperback she'd bought at the station bookstall. She hadn't had much time for reading since going to London, almost a year ago.

Living and working in the city had proved even more exciting than she'd ever imagined. She had so much to tell her father, and her sister, too, if she'd time to listen.

When news of Alison's engagement and planned May wedding had reached Helen in London, she hadn't been surprised. Her sister had been dating Keith for over three years.

"I'd like you to wear blue with a touch of white, Helen, if you can find something," Alison had said dreamily down the phone. "And a hat! A nice floppy picture hat . . ."

"A hat!" Helen had interrupted. "Must I? Half my life I have to wear a hat — it's the only thing about nursing I dislike."

"Well, if you really don't want to . . ." Alison had sounded disappointed.

"Oh, all right, seeing it's for you, love." Helen gave in gracefully.

"Thanks, I knew you would. And you can wear heels as high as you like," her sister had continued enthusiastically. "Because Ricky's best man."

RICKY, Dr Richard Brown — Helen spoke the name softly to herself as the train sped on its way, every mile now taking her closer to the small home-town she'd abandoned in favour of the bright lights of London.

They'd gone to school together, she and Ricky. He'd been in Upper Sixth when she'd been doing her "O"-levels.

"When we qualify, we'll go to London and work together in the same hospital," she'd enthused then and Ricky had nodded in agreement, laughter in his blue eyes.

He went off to medical school and she began her nurse-training at the local hospital. They met up whenever he was home on vacation and she was off duty. She had always confided in Ricky, telling him of her dreams of getting away to London, assuming that they were still his dreams too.

But, once qualified, he'd chosen to return to Crompton and was now junior partner in a group medical practice. He'd said nothing to sway her decision to go to London; and since finally going, and meeting Howard, Ricky's place in her life had become one of fond memories.

They knew about Howard back home, of course, and he'd been invited to her sister's wedding, but at the very last moment he'd got wind of some V.I.P.s flying in from Brussels. He was sorry to let Helen down, but he'd have to be there to meet them.

After her initial disappointment, Helen had felt an indefinable sense of relief.

Howard was in business in the city, and so much a "townie" that she might have felt awkward bringing him here to the slower way of life in Crompton.

The train was slowing, and glancing out of the window, she recognised the familiar countryside and the embankment, now awash with bluebells and wild parsley.

Alison had promised to be there to meet her, and as it was to be an afternoon wedding, Helen had done little to dissuade her. True to her word, her sister was there and it wasn't long before they were hugging each other happily while fellow passengers on the small platform jostled around them.

YOU look different!'' Alison held Helen at arm's length. ''Sort of sophisticated.'' She put her unruly curly-haired head to one side. ''It's your hair,'' she decided. ''You've had it cut. Whatever will Dad say?''

Grabbing Helen's small suitcase, Alison led her through the ticket barrier to a white Mini parked alongside the kerb.

''How *is* Dad?'' Helen asked, as they drove off down the High Street.

''At sixes and sevens with all the wedding plans.'' She giggled. ''This morning he made a pot of tea and forgot to put the tea in!'' Her face became serious. ''It's a pity you were only able to get two days off. Dad would have enjoyed having you to himself.''

Helen felt a pang of guilt. She hadn't told her sister that she was flying off on holiday to Greece with Howard whenever she got back to London.

''You and Keith have got a house in Queen's Road, did you say?'' she asked, deciding to make no comment.

''Yes. A couple of minutes from Dad, that's all.'' Alison smiled.

Their father was awaiting their arrival in the glass vestibule, surrounded by beanstalk-high tomato plants.

Helen felt a shadow fall over the brightness of the day as she noticed the change in her father's appearance. Was it really only a year since she'd gone away, she asked herself in dismay.

He was holding her now and she was struck by the coldness of his face against hers, despite the heat of the day.

''I've missed you, Lena.'' It was barely a whisper and if she hadn't seen his lips moving, she'd have wondered if she'd imagined the words. No-one had called her by her pet name for a very long time.

''Oh, Dad, it's lovely to be home.'' She squeezed his hand and tried to keep her voice steady, her thoughts in turmoil. She'd make a point of getting home after this, she vowed. Perhaps for his birthday, and maybe at Christmas, too. But remembering the whirl of parties last year she knew she mustn't make a promise which she couldn't keep.

THE house was just as if she'd never been away. The spell of unusually warm weather had brought the lilac into bloom and its heavy scent drifted in through the open windows.

In no time at all Helen had a cup of coffee in her hand, and her father and sister were talking to her, interrupting each other in their eagerness to give her all their news.

Her father was telling her about his old friends down at the bowling green, then about Keith and what a fine lad he was.

Alison couldn't wait to tell her sister about the wedding presents they'd received, and the music for the church service. ''Do hurry with that coffee — I'm longing to show you my dress,'' she urged impatiently.

"It's gorgeous!" Helen stood in the doorway of her sister's room, gazing with frank admiration at the beautiful gown of white broderie anglaise which Alison had laid carefully on her bed.

"Something old." Alison picked up the frothy veil from its place on the pillow. "This was mother's," she said with reverence, "and shall be put away for you.

"Something new — my dress; something borrowed . . ." She showed Helen a pair of lacy gloves. "And something blue . . ." Alison clasped her hands together. "You'll probably think I'm crazy and terribly unsophisticated, but I don't like bouquets, not formal ones. I'm having instead a nosegay of forget-me-nots and lilies-of-the-valley."

"That's lovely." Helen nodded approvingly, remembering the carpeted embankment of bluebells whose light fragrance had drifted in through the carriage windows of the train on her journey home.

Almost immediately other memories flitted into her mind. She found herself picturing the expensive orchid from Covent Garden which Howard had brought her for her birthday — and the cultured roses he had presented to her at Christmas.

She remembered, too, attending the wedding of one of his colleagues and the bride's magnificent bouquet of stiff carnations.

"Now *your* dress — I'm longing to see it." Alison was undoing the catches on her sister's suitcase.

"I must admit, I'm hoping I'll be able to wear the dress later for evening dates." Helen tossed a tissue-wrapped, floppy hat on the bed, then carefully lifted out of its wrapping a soft lawn-cotton dress with delicate trimmings of lace.

"That's perfect!" Alison said dreamily. "I couldn't have chosen better myself."

S O the events of the day progressed. There was little to do at home as the reception was in a small hotel. Most of the guests lived locally and were going straight to the church.

Mr Carter, the girls' father, was nervous about his part in the wedding ceremony. He told Helen the same story about a bowling incident at least three times, and twice insisted on taking her round the garden to show her the new rose bushes he'd planted.

"Just look at these beauties, Lena, they were your mother's favourites, you know." There was a catch in his voice. "I only wish she'd been here today. It doesn't seem right . . ." His voice tailed away emotionally.

"Now, Dad," Helen said firmly, taking his cold hand in hers.

"You mustn't go upsetting yourself, not today, of all days."

"No, no," he mumbled, then dropping her hand he looked at her through moist eyes. "Why d'you cut your hair, lass?" he whispered.

"Oh, it's fashionable just now," she volunteered, not wanting to tell him that it was Howard who'd suggested she have it cut in readiness for their holiday.

He grunted disapprovingly and walked towards his greenhouse.

"Besides, it'll grow again," she called after him, hating the feeling that she had disappointed him.

At lunchtime Helen noticed her father picking at his food, then pushing his plate away as soon as Alison left the room.

"Are you all right, Dad?" she asked carefully, noticing the beads of perspiration on his forehead.

"Of course I am," he snapped, so sharply that Helen's eyes widened in surprise. "I suppose it's wedding nerves . . ." he added more gently.

Helen sighed — her father had never spoken to her like that before. There was a time when she was doing her nursing training when he used to share his every little ache and pain with her. She'd reassure him and they'd end up laughing about it together — but that was before she went away to work in London.

The sound of the "Wedding March" filled the whole church as Alison made her way slowly and carefully down the aisle on her father's arm, to join Keith and Ricky who had taken their places a few moments before.

Helen was momentarily distracted from studying her father's faltering steps by the sight of the two men waiting at the altar.

Keith, with his unmistakable dark, curly hair above square shoulders, seemed to be dwarfed by the figure alongside, who stood head and shoulders above him.

FRAGRANT MEMORIES

*I*N *Mary's garden blooms a rose,
its glory spans each summertime.
"A rose to remember me," said Lucy,
when she came to say goodbye, ere
leaving to marry in New Zealand.*

*Under Mary's care that rose has
thrived; so too her contact with Lucy.
Rose and relationship have flourished down the years.*

*"I will make a garden of friendship!"
Mary resolved.*

*When those she had not seen for
years came to visit. "Bring me a rose
for my garden," she would ask, "that
thoughts of you may blossom there."*

*So when Mary strolls through her
roses, she walks amongst fragrant
memories of friendships she tends with
green fingers in the garden of her heart.*

Rev. T. R. S. Campbell.

Ricky Brown had changed little over the years, except perhaps for his thick hair, which appeared even blonder than before. A sudden wave of shyness stopped Helen from meeting his gaze as she took her place by Alison's side.

Listening almost dreamily to the familiar words of the marriage ceremony, Helen wondered how long it would be before Howard would ask her to marry him. She'd half hoped, if he'd been here today, the mood and the magic of it all . . .

Her thoughts were interrupted as Alison's nosegay was handed to her. The fragrance of the flowers rose to her nostrils and a vision appeared in her mind. A dark-haired girl and a tall, fair young man were running barefoot through woods carpeted with bluebells.

Then suddenly it was replaced by the picture of an affluent young man in a pin-striped suit, handing her an orchid.

SOON everyone was outside the church, standing in the bright sunlight. The photographer was moving them around, asking them to smile. Ricky was there, with his arm around Helen's shoulders one minute, then kissing the bride the next.

They were standing beneath a flowering cherry tree, and a gentle breeze rustled its branches, showering them with pink blossom. Ricky strode over and lightly blew away the petals that had come to rest on her large hat. Helen was disturbed when she found herself having to check the bubbles of excitement rising within her at his nearness.

Yet, all the while, she was aware of her father and the look of lost bewilderment on his pale face.

"Cheer up, old man," Uncle Mike was saying. "You're not losing a daughter, but gaining a son!"

Then the wedding party left for the reception and Helen was in the back seat of a taxi, her father on one side and Ricky on the other. He was grinning boyishly at her and she burst out laughing when he removed her hat and put it on his own head. All at once, it was like it used to be, as if the time in between had never been.

She found herself searching among the guests for some young woman who appeared to be with him, someone she may not even know, but there seemed to be no-one who might fit the picture.

Family and friends whom she hadn't seen in the last year were eager to greet her and bring her up to date with their news.

"Come on, Helen." Ricky was carefully edging her away from a group of old acquaintances. "It's half an hour since Alison and Keith went to change into their going-away clothes. I promised we'd follow, bring them back here to make their farewells, then drive them to the airport."

YOU'D better tell me a little about this London you've come to love so much." Ricky spoke while keeping his gaze on the road ahead as they made their way back from the airport.

Helen had been longing, ever since arriving home, to tell someone how she really felt about London. Yet now that Ricky had asked her point blank, she felt a moment's doubt about her life there.

"Well, life there is so exciting and fast!" She tried to sound enthusiastic. "It's so vital, so real, I just love it . . ." She finished rather weakly.

"Love *it*? Or is it some*one* there you love?" Despite the directness of the question, Ricky's voice never lost its hint of amusement.

Helen was flustered. Everyone up to now had been too preoccupied to ask her about anything precise, like Howard, for instance. She'd forgotten just how frank Ricky had always been.

"I love . . . London I guess," she offered, trying to sound sincere.

"The smog?" he asked derisively. "The crowds? The rush-hour? You really love all that?" He sounded surprised.

"Oh, there's more to London than all that," she retorted defensively. "There are theatres and parks and the Thames and . . ."

But she didn't finish. They'd pulled up in the car-park of the small hotel to find a group of wedding guests standing anxiously around the doorway.

Instead of parking, Ricky drew alongside.

"Something wrong?" he asked, obviously not really expecting there to be, from the laughter in his voice.

"I'm afraid so." Uncle Mike stepped forward and looked into the car directly at Helen. "It's your father, lass. Not long after you'd left with Alison and Keith. He collapsed."

"Oh, no!" A wave of fear washed over Helen and she gripped the leather seat of the car, bracing herself.

"We sent for an ambulance," Uncle Mike was saying. "They were here within minutes."

H OLD tight." Ricky's voice was calm, authoritative now. He gripped Helen's hand and squeezed it reassuringly then revved up the engine and drove swiftly out on to the road in the direction of the hospital.

When they got there, Helen and Ricky were shown into a small waiting-room, where they were soon joined by a young house doctor who had been at the same school as they had.

"I'm sorry to meet you under such sad circumstances, Helen. Your father's had a heart attack."

"How bad?" she asked apprehensively, pulling nervously at the straw brim of the hat she now held in her hands.

"Difficult to say at this stage," the doctor replied. "He's conscious, but very drowsy after treatment. I don't need to tell you that the next few hours may well decide . . ."

"I'll stay, of course," Helen said quickly.

"Let me run you home to get changed," Ricky offered. "It could be a long night — and cold."

She looked down at her dress.

"I'd quite forgotten about that! Thanks." She turned to him. "But I'd really rather not leave, just in case."

He didn't insist, and after going with her to her father's bedside he slipped quietly away.

It was around midnight when one of the nurses slipped a cloak around her shoulders.

"Dr Brown's here to see you. He's in the kitchen. I've made some coffee for you both."

Ricky had changed from his smart wedding clothes and was in jeans and a big chunky sweater.

"Will you let me take over?" he urged. "Go home and get some rest." He handed her a cup of steaming coffee.

"I couldn't." She stirred her coffee, afraid to meet his gaze. "I just want to be here."

"What about Alison?" he asked quietly.

"She mustn't be told," Helen said without hesitation. "Not unless — not unless . . ." There was a catch in her voice.

"Let's cross that bridge if and when we have to." Ricky's voice in the intimacy of the warm kitchen was comforting. "But if you're going back to London tomorrow, you'll *have* to get some rest."

"No, I couldn't, really. Besides, I'm not tired." She pulled the cloak around her and shivered.

"Very well." He moved to the door and paused. "Please call me if there's anything I can do."

"Thanks, Ricky," she whispered without looking up, and then he was gone and she was alone again.

B ACK at her father's bedside she continued her vigil. Once or twice he opened his eyes and she watched him struggling to get her into focus then murmuring her name before drifting off again.

By the time the first light of morning was breaking through, her father's condition had stabilised and he was looking a little brighter. Just before the increased ward activity heralded the arrival of day staff, he raised his arm and reached out towards her.

Helen took his hand in hers as he raised it weakly to her cropped hair.

"Did you say you'd grow it?" he managed drowsily.

Her eyes brimmed over.

"I did, and I shall," she promised, clasping his hand in both of hers and holding it gently to her cheek.

Then she had to leave while they attended to her father.

T HAT was when Helen had made her way to the woods nearby. Having reached their sanctuary she had taken off her shoes so that she might feel again the freedom of walking barefoot on the dew-damp grass.

By now she'd reached the narrow path which ran along the side of the stream. The air here was heavy with the scent of the wild flowers, and the thick blue carpet of bluebells stretched away to one side.

Her jumbled thoughts began to take shape, to form a pattern. She'd ask for compassionate leave from the hospital where she worked until her father was out of danger. Until Alison and Keith returned from their honeymoon. When her father recovered, the young couple would be able to care for him without difficulty.

Yet, looking around her now, though Helen knew she could easily justify her eventual return to London, the desire to do so had died within her.

Had she really forfeited all this natural beauty for the artificial glamour of a city? What of Howard? Where did he really fit into all this? Could she imagine *him* ever running barefoot in these woods?

Life here in Crompton had gone on undisturbed by her absence. No doubt it would do so once again if she were to leave. But though everyone here could get along very well without her, Helen knew without doubt that she could never get along without them. □

A T dusk one autumn afternoon Mrs Jean Meikle answered a ring at her door.

A tall young man, a suitcase at his feet, stood waiting. He had a thatch of hair the colour of ripe wheat and a sun-browned face which now held an anxious look.

"Mrs Meikle?" he asked hesitantly. "I've been told you have a vacant room for a student. I got your name from . . ."

"Then they'd no right to give you my name," Jean Meikle broke in. "I told the agency to take my address off their books." She was dismayed at the sharpness of her voice, but she was upset.

By
ANNE
WATSON

"I'm sorry you're giving up," the nice lady in the agency had said. "Our boys will miss you, Mrs Meikle. Still, health comes first, we're poor souls without it."

Jean Meikle had agreed half heartedly. The truth was she didn't really want to give up being a students' landlady. She had made her decision because of pressure from other folk.

Dr Polson, for instance.

"Now look, Mrs Meikle, you've had a very nasty shake, and your leg is never going to be right if you keep running up and down stairs after your students. You must take a rest."

The good doctor was right, of course. Since her accident Jean had to admit she felt shaky and less able to cope with the busy daily round which having students involved.

"You must do what Dr Polson says." More pressure, this time from her friend and neighbour, Maisie Stoddart. "You're due a long holiday, you've been taking in students for as long as I've known you, Jean."

"For close on twenty years," Jean had replied.

She had first opened her house to her "boys" soon after her husband, Henry, had died. She enjoyed housework, loved to bake and cook, and had always been fond of the company of young folk, though she and Henry, sadly, had not had any family of their own.

Jean hadn't fancied living on alone in the big, old-fashioned top flat in Edinburgh's Abbeyhill. The two spacious attic bedrooms were just the very thing for students and right from the word go the project had turned out well. The extra money was welcome, too.

Echo Of Long Ago

B UT that was before she had slipped on the attic stairs and taken a bad tumble earlier in the year. Thankfully, wee Jean had suffered no broken bones, only bad bruising, but the shock to her nerves had been considerable.

"Can you give up, Mrs Meikle?" Dr Polson had asked frankly, in the kindest possible way, "I mean, can you *afford* to take, say, a year off?"

"Oh, yes, doctor. I could manage," Jean had assured him.

Didn't she have Henry's small pension, as well as quite a wee nest-egg put by from all her years of hard work? She had always thought these savings were for a rainy day, and now that rainy day had come.

"I miss them, Maisie," Jean confided to her neighbour. "I find my days hard to fill, and I'm sorry for Teerie." Jean's wee Border terrier was certainly missing young company, and the outings he'd grown used to.

But Mrs Stoddart was unsympathetic.

"I wish *I* had some time to myself! Between the shop, the house, Alec and Rosemary — and Hero—I'm only too ready to flop into my bed most nights. Some folk don't know when they're lucky!"

The Stoddarts owned a busy corner shop that seemed to stay open day and night as well as weekends, and it was true Maisie was kept busy there serving beside her husband, Alec.

Rosemary was their only child, nearly seventeen and still at school. She was a lovely girl and she had lots of boys wanting to date her.

But Rosemary Stoddart was choosey; "I like boys with some grey-matter in their heads, Mum," she would say. "I like a boy who knows where he's going." She seemed content to go for long walks with Hero, the Stoddart's black Alsatian, or to bury her nose in a book.

S PRING-CLEAN your box-room," Maisie advised. "That'll keep you busy." And Jean did as she was told. It was there, at the back of an old trunk, and undisturbed for years, she unearthed the old photograph album.

Somehow Jean felt she didn't want to look through the crowded pages on her own, so she waited till one evening when Maisie had popped in to keep her company.

The two friends sat side by side on Jean's sofa and shared the album. There were snapshots of long-ago picnics, weddings, holidays, all taken in or around the small village in Wester Ross where Jean had been born and lived her first thirteen years. "See this one, that's Cathy MacKenzie, my best chum — what a head of hair. Cathy would boast she could sit on it!" she exclaimed.

"And look, Maisie, that's our Sunday school picnic to Gairloch sands, that's me in the trendy swimsuit."

They came to a group taken in a school playground.

"That's my qualifying class. I was twelve then and, soon after, we left Drumm to come and live in Edinburgh. My father had joined the Midlothian Police."

Jean's finger pointed to a plump boy in the front row of the picture.

"That's Robbie MacKenzie. We called him The Professor — he was the headmaster's son and won all the prizes."

"Another MacKenzie!" Maisie laughed.

"Oh, yes, we were nearly all MacKenzies in Drumm!" Jean's finger lingered over the faded school photograph.

"See this first one in the back row, he was a MacKenzie, too. 'Big Alasdair-of-the-few-words,' we called him, for he had the name of being shy. But he wasn't all that shy!"

Jean smiled a secret smile to herself when she remembered it was Big Alasdair who had invited her to the school leavers' party all those years ago in Drumm.

"You'll be my partner, Jean?" he'd asked her.

"Well, maybe," she had replied.

"What's maybe? Will you or won't you?"

"All right then, Alasdair, I will."

He had taken her in for supper, and stood close beside wee Jean for the flashlight photograph. And the big, dark lad was waiting for her, too, when the party was over.

"I'll walk you home, Jean." And halfway to Jean's cottage he had taken her hand. "I wish you were staying on in Drumm."

At her door, he had put strong arms around her and planted a self-conscious kiss on her rosy cheek. "I'll remember this night, Jean," he had promised.

Later, when the photographs of the school party were given out, Big Alasdair had carefully cut his in two, then he had given one half to Jean.

"You keep me, Jean, and I'll keep you."

JEAN hadn't seen the dark-eyed boy again nor had she been back to Drumm. She had become a children's nurse and met and married Henry Meikle.

The echo of that first tender brush with young love had lingered with her though, and the sight of the old photograph stirred memories which made her eyes moisten suspiciously.

It had all been so long ago, she told herself, you're being sentimental. Today was what mattered most.

And today, at this moment, Mrs Jean Meikle stood beside her open front door, face to face with this young student seeking a room.

"I just don't understand how that agency told you I was still taking in folk." But the wee landlady's voice was plainly softening and had totally lost its first sharp edge.

"Perhaps you would know of another address where I . . . ?"

Jean shook her head, realising that in a moment he would be gone. She didn't want to hear his footsteps fade away, out of her life   there was something about this young man — she had taken to him already.

"Wait!" she cried out. "What's your name?"

"Drew, Drew MacKenzie." Another MacKenzie!

"Do you come from Wester Ross, the same as I do, Drew?"

"No, I was brought up in Caithness. But you never know, perhaps my roots are in Wester Ross." He smiled hopefully.

"I've changed my mind, Drew. Come in." Jean opened the door wide. "I think you'll get on fine here; I'll show you up to your room."

TEERIE took to Drew MacKenzie right away. The young man had only to shake the lead to send the dog skidding down the lobby to the front door, yelping with joy. As autumn gave way to winter, Jean Meikle's new student more or less took charge of Teerie.

Every evening at half-past nine Drew would close his books, tidy his papers and pens away, and take up the dog's lead.

An hour's jog with Teerie was the best cure for too much study, he told his landlady. He had got into the habit of going off with Teerie on a Sunday, as well, to the Pentland Hills or to Craigie Quarries.

"It's a long time since the dog's been so happy," Jean remarked to Maisie Stoddart. "Drew has a great way with Teerie."

Maisie hadn't quite got over her first impatience with her friend for taking in another student.

"Wait till Dr Polson hears about this!" she had scolded Jean.

"But I'm a whole lot better for the lad's company," Jean had protested. "I was getting too depressed, Maisie, harking back to the past far too much. Anyway, Drew's not much work, he's a quiet lad."

"He certainly is," Maisie had agreed. "If you meet him on the stair, he hasn't a word to say for himself — not even to our Rosemary. Not that Rosemary's bothered," she had added hastily. "A country boy like Drew is the last kind of boyfriend she would choose!"

Jean had forced herself to remain silent, although she longed to spring to his defence.

"Do you know any more about him than you did when he first came?" Maisie had then asked, curiously.

"Yes, of course I do — he's studying to be a computer specialist." The words had a nice ring to them, Jean had thought.

"I meant do you know any more about his background?" Maisie had persisted.

But Jean still knew very little about Drew. He got very few letters.

"That's because my father is away at sea," he had explained one day to a concerned Jean. "I was brought up by my grandparents on their croft in Caithness. Now they're both gone, who is there to write to me?" he had explained matter of factly.

Mrs Meikle secretly admired the young lad for his quiet acceptance of a life without a single close relation — except a father who was a ship's engineer at the other side of the world.

WOULD you let me stay on here with you over my holidays?" Drew shyly asked Jean as Christmas drew near.

"But what about your father, Drew?" Delighted as she was by his request, Jean didn't want to come between them. "Does he never get home to Scotland for a holiday?"

"Oh, he's been home this year. He had a leave in the summer, just before I came to you," Drew explained. "But now he's with an oil tanker off the coast of Queensland."

Soon after that conversation took place, a fat letter bearing a Christmas seal, as well as the Australian postmark, arrived for Drew.

Jean handed it over to the lad as pleased as Punch for him.

"It's from my father!"

"I hope it's good news — I hope he's well," Jean ventured.

Drew was already bounding upstairs to his room, where he sat on his bed. It took him a long time to go over the contents of the Christmas envelope, then he did something which would have astonished Maisie Stoddart.

The shy, young student from the country leapt high in the air and fairly whooped with triumphant joy!

The week before Christmas saw Edinburgh shrouded in a freezing fog. It was Sunday at lunchtime when the sun suddenly appeared, looking for all the world like a bright blood-orange in the sky.

"Come on, wee Teerie, we're off!" Drew rattled the lead and Teerie turned a complete somersault in his excitement to be off.

"Remember, lad, it's dark early," Jean Meikle warned Drew. "Don't go too far, now."

"Don't worry," he assured her. "We'll be back before five, that's a promise."

> ## For Ever . . .
>
> **T**RUE friendship is a stalwart plant.
>   It will not fade and die
> When cold winds blow and sombre clouds
>   Chase sunshine from the sky.
>
> Through summer's warmth and winter's chill
>   Its precious seed matures —
> True friendship is a hardy bloom
>   That steadfastly endures.
>
>   *Eileen Thomas.*

Jean took advantage of the quiet spell to fetch out the old Christmas tree. She set it up at the sitting-room window, and fixed the silver and gold baubles, the stars and the fairy doll that were brought out every December.

Suddenly, when Jean was admiring the finished result of her efforts, she glanced at the clock. It was after five o'clock, surely Drew and Teerie should have been back by now.

But when six o'clock struck, then half-past, Jean Meikle went shakily to fetch her coat. She must go to the local police station, she decided.

She was about to close the door behind her when she heard hurrying footsteps coming quickly up the long stairs. It must be Drew, it must be, she thought thankfully.

It wasn't her quiet young student and wee Teerie, however, who appeared in a few moments.

Rosemary Stoddart stood there with Hero, her Alsatian dog.

"I've a message from Drew, Mrs Meikle. You're not to worry, he'll be all right," she blurted out.

Poor Jean, her head seemed to spin like a top. *Where was Drew and what had Maisie's daughter to do with him?*

"You've seen him?" Jean gasped, unable to hide her amazement.

"I've just left him," was the surprising reply. "We'd been for our usual Sunday hike — the four of us. We meet up at the park most week-ends and take the dogs up to the Pentlands or to Craigie Quarries . . ." The young girl rattled on at such a speed she was scarcely coherent.

Jean's fears for Drew's safety mounted.

"But where is he? Where's Drew?" she asked anxiously.

She urged Rosemary to come into the house and then the tale was haltingly told.

THE two young folk had taken the woodland walk to the disused quarries. The dogs loved this walk where they could sniff out rabbits, and dash through drifting heaps of autumn leaves, racing each other when they came into an open stretch.

"But all at once," Rosemary explained, "the mist came back down and we could scarcely see a thing. Drew said we must get home at once, so we called the dogs. But Teerie never appeared, although we could hear him — we could hear his far-off squeals and whimpers."

Drew and Rosemary had soon realised that Teerie's desperate cries for help came from the direction of the old quarry. The young student had told the girl to stay where she was while he went off on his own to look for Teerie.

Darkness fell, the fog crept close, and it had seemed to Rosemary as if she had waited through a whole long night, though in reality it was scarcely fifteen minutes.

Then she had heard Drew MacKenzie's voice.

"Rosemary!" he had called out. "I'm stuck here and it's too dangerous to move in the dark. Teerie's trapped somewhere near me, down in the quarry.

"Get home at once, love. Tell Mrs Meikle I'll be all right, but get help," he had ordered.

Rosemary continued her story.

"I made it back with Hero's help, but I'm so worried about Drew, and poor little Teerie . . ." Her voice broke as reaction to her ordeal set in.

Jean hurried to set the rescue wheels in motion.

Young and fit as he undoubtedly was, the hours spent in the freezing fog of a December night took their toll of Drew MacKenzie.

He was rushed to hospital by a waiting ambulance. It was fully daylight before Jean Meikle's wee Border terrier was at last found, trapped in a rabbit hole. So Teerie Meikle found himself in the famous Edinburgh hospital for sick animals for several days.

Drew was kept in hospital for three days, fuming all the while.

"The fuss he's making you'd think they were asking him to stay in for three years," Jean remarked to Rosemary.

"It's just that he's desperate to be back with you for Christmas Day," Rosemary defended her boyfriend.

"Then if that's all he's bothered about, I'm surprised at him," Jean remarked, inwardly delighted. She wasn't to know that Drew had other private reasons, shared only with Rosemary, for wanting to be home by Christmas Day.

Two days before Christmas Eve, he was discharged from hospital. He went out to buy lights for Jean's Christmas tree and that evening Rosemary came in to help him to arrange them. She stayed on to give Mrs Meikle a hand with preparations for the Christmas meal, which Jean had invited the Stoddarts to share.

B UT to Jean, Christmas this year seemed to have lost a lot of its old magic.

She felt strangely cut off from everyone.

Once or twice she had come across Rosemary and Drew whispering with their heads close together, and stopping quickly as soon as Jean had appeared. And Alec, Maisie's husband, was kind and attentive to his wife. Even Teerie was being made a great fuss of by the Stoddarts' Alsatian, Hero.

Try as she might Jean couldn't throw off this sudden feeling of isolation in a world where others were paired off so happily.

O N the morning of Christmas Eve Jean went shopping and, on her way back through Abbeyhill, noticed that the doors of her own church were open wide, almost as if she were being willed to enter.

On an impulse, she went inside, finding the church crowded with children.

Small Brownies were busily decorating the deep window-ledges with holly and mistletoe, while some Girl Guides were setting out the Nativity tableau with its crib, the three kings, the shepherds, the Holy family, and the animals.

The feeling of isolation from all this happy activity suddenly overwhelmed Jean. When her eyes filled with tears, she bowed her head low to hide them, and then a very strange thing happened.

Like a spring of cool water rising up within her, Jean was enveloped by a wonderful peace. She imagined she could hear a soft voice telling her: *You are not alone, I am with you always.*

Jean Meikle remained seated for a moment or two more. When at last she raised her head and opened her moist eyes, a brightness seemed to fill the old church, a brightness which was reflected on the happy faces of the busy young people. She knew the interlude of stillness in her beloved place of worship had wrought its own Christmas miracle for her.

When at last Jean tackled the long tenement stair to her home her heart was lighter than it had been for weeks past.

D REW MACKENZIE was up early on Christmas morning. He took his landlady a cup of tea on a tray, along with an envelope and a brightly-wrapped parcel.

"What's this, Drew?" Jean queried with a smile.

"I think Santa has called in the night!" he teased her.

Jean's hands went first to the envelope, but the young student stopped her as she made to open it.

"Not that, it's probably just another card — open the parcel!"

The festive wrappings on the parcel opened to reveal a pair of fur-lined slippers, the height of luxury. There was a gift tag attached with the message: *From Drew MacKenzie to a Wonderful Friend.*

"Happy Christmas, Mrs M." Drew planted a kiss on Jean's flushed face. "I'll leave you to open the envelope on your own." And he was gone from her room with astonishing speed.

JEAN sipped her tea slowly, looking admiringly at Drew's gift. She was about to get up when her eye caught the envelope still unopened on her tray. She stared at the unfamiliar writing — could it be a Christmas card handed in by one of the neighbours? She opened it unhurriedly.

The next moment Jean Meikle was stumbling out of bed, out of the bedroom.

"Drew MacKenzie, are you there?"

He came through from the kitchen, cool as a cucumber.

"Will you tell me what this is all about, Drew?" she demanded, waving the envelope under his nose.

"Oh, that! It's from my dad." Drew grinned down at her. "He enclosed it with a letter I got a few weeks ago.

"He told me when he was home on his last leave he knew you once when you were a wee lassie up in Drumm. The two of you had your photos taken at a school party. He found out you were still in Edinburgh and all on your own . . ." Drew began to chuckle.

"You know something, Mrs M.?" he confessed. "It wasn't that Student's Agency that gave me your address — it was my father, Big Alasdair MacKenzie!"

As one expression after another flitted over Jean's face, Drew put his arms around her.

"Don't be angry, please," he pleaded, hugging the little woman close to him. "It's just that Dad's eager to see you again. He thought sending you that old photo might do the trick."

THE envelope had indeed held a Christmas card — but one with a very special difference! Framed like a small picture by holly and Christmas roses was a much-handled photograph of a young girl. She had straight fair hair worn in a fringe, bonnie blue eyes, and she was wearing a pretty party dress.

It was the photograph of wee Jean herself, taken so long ago!

Written on the inner page of the card in a big, bold hand were the words: *Happy Christmas, wee Jean. I'll be back to see you at Easter-time. But write to me, write to me soon. Big Alasdair.*

"You never thought this would happen when you took me in, Mrs M.!" Drew exclaimed.

"Maybe I did," Jean whispered. "I think I've been listening for that lingering echo of love for a long time, Drew." □

Lucky In Love

by Grace Macaulay

R UTH GILCHRIST paused, holding the telephone receiver against her ear with one hand while her other hand hovered uncertainly.

It was almost as if it were unwilling to obey her instruction to dial the number which was in her mind.

If you do phone Stuart, she cautioned herself, you could be starting along a path which will lead to goodbye. On the other hand, Ruth argued silently, if you don't phone him, everything will probably remain exactly the same. Is that what I really want, she wondered.

Her left hand moved slightly, as if she had decided against the idea, and there was the faint metallic sound of her engagement ring coming into contact with the receiver.

99

Yes, that ring will stay on your finger, the dialling tone so close to her ear seemed to be saying — Stuart loves you. He won't throw you over just because some girl happened to catch his eye last night, and he danced with her.

All right, so he had lunch with her today, Ruth's troubled thoughts ran on. But would you ever have known if a so-called friend hadn't told you?

Ruth could imagine Stuart's reaction when she spoke to him about it.

"You shouldn't let people upset you, Ruth, darling," he would say tenderly. "Don't you realise that some people enjoy causing trouble?"

Then he would take her in his arms and hold her close.

"That's what I love about you, Ruth, you believe that the world is full of good people. I'd never like to see you being hurt because of your trusting nature." His smile would be gentle.

"Once we're married, darling, I'll take care of you. Every minute of every day, I'll be looking after you, loving you . . ."

ABRUPTLY, Ruth jerked herself back to reality and began to dial Stuart's number. She didn't know why she felt this urge to speak to him. She'd never been good at analysing her emotions — she only knew that she had to see him soon. Risk or no risk, she couldn't endure this uncertainty.

"Hello." Stuart's voice sounded abrupt.

"It's me," she said, timidly. "Were you busy? Did I interrupt . . . ?"

"Ruth! Of course not!" Now his voice was filled with warmth. "I was only watching television."

Did she imagine a slight hesitation? She wished he had added that he would much sooner talk to her than watch any television programme.

Ruth hurriedly began to explain to him that her mother wanted a parcel delivered to an elderly lady in Dundas Street.

"So I thought I'd pop in and see you, seeing it's just around the corner from you." Ruth tried to make her suggestion as casual as she possibly could. "That's only if you happen to have coffee in your cupboard, of course!" she joked.

"I have coffee!" He laughed into the phone. "How soon will you be here?"

"In about half an hour," she answered. "That'll give me time for a nice chat with Mum's old friend."

Ruth took the parcel from her mother a few seconds later.

"Thanks, Mum, I'll do my best with Mrs Wilmott."

Mrs Gilchrist pursed her lips, frowning for a moment.

"She doesn't really mean to be cantankerous," she said. "It's just that she hates the idea of accepting presents."

She looked at Ruth questioningly.

"Why won't you tell me what's wrong, dear? You look upset."

When Ruth didn't respond, she continued.

"I could drive over and drop you off at Stuart's place, then go on to Mrs Wilmott's house myself."

Ruth flushed under her mother's keen scrutiny.

"Maybe I'll tell you about it when I come back . . . You know I offered to deliver your parcel so that I'd have an excuse to see Stuart.

"I didn't tell him I'd offered." She shrugged helplessly, unable to go into more detail, unsure of her own feelings.

"But he wouldn't know if I just dropped you off at his place." Mrs Gilchrist was puzzled by Ruth's reply.

"It would make my excuse a lie." Ruth's voice faltered. "I thought you understood that, Mum. I needed an excuse, an honest reason." She smiled tremulously.

Impulsively, her mother hugged her unhappy daughter.

"All right, Ruth," she agreed. "I'll just go and finish off that weeding in the back garden."

With a reminiscent smile, she thought of the noisy, teenage years of her two sons who were now happily married. They were rather staid professional men, she thought indulgently. Just like their father, whom she now found dozing on the sun-lounger in the garden.

Her husband glanced up at her as she approached and with a rueful smile she sat down beside him, letting the gardening gloves lie on her lap. With a wonder which never ceased to thrill her, she realised just how well he understood her.

"There's something wrong between Ruth and Stuart," she told him.

"I do hope she isn't planning to give him back his ring." Her brow furrowed anxiously.

George Gilchrist groaned. "Oh no! Not with the wedding only weeks away!" He reached over and gently patted her hand. "Surely you aren't serious, Madge? I mean, Ruth wouldn't do anything impulsive, she's such a sensible girl."

"Ruth is so sensitive." Madge Gilchrist sighed as she picked up her gloves. "Anyhow, I'm going to do some weeding."

George yawned and stretched.

"I should really cut the grass," he said, his wife's energy making him feel guilty.

"Maybe Ruth *is* sensitive, but it's not a fault, Madge. You know as well as I do that she's made of sterner stuff than anyone would give her credit for. Remember the time . . ."

B UT his wife wasn't listening any more, she was already almost out of earshot.

Well, he thought, rising reluctantly to his feet, I'd better fetch out that lawnmower.

He hoped that his wife was wrong about Ruth, he mused, as he went towards the garden shed. Surely she wouldn't break with Stuart, not when they were so obviously suited to each other. They were a sensible pair . . . his idle thoughts came to an abrupt halt. Maybe a young couple in love ought not to be labelled with the description "sensible."

RUTH hadn't been particularly attracted to Stuart at first. It wasn't until the third time they met, at a dance, that he had asked her to go out with him.

In those first months their dates had been almost casual and for a while Ruth had even wondered if Stuart only rang her up when he had nothing better to do.

But gradually their friendship had flowered into a companionable kind of love. At twenty-four, Ruth had abandoned the idea that a single glance across a crowded room would flame into an ecstatic love.

Reasonably and sensibly, she had accepted Stuart's proposal of marriage and when she thought of their future, she saw the two of them as partners in a comfortable, well-ordered life.

Even last night at that party, she hadn't foreseen any shadows on her future. She was well aware that Stuart was a good-looking man. Why shouldn't a girl want to flirt with him?

Ruth rang his doorbell now with a trembling finger, aware that her heart was fluttering alarmingly. A confrontation of this kind went against her natural instincts, as well as her better judgment.

Sternly she told herself that she must remain cool and wait for Stuart to mention the lunch date with the girl. She had a feeling that if he didn't tell her about it she would blurt out the accusing questions which were tumbling around in her mind.

In the few seconds before he came to the door, Ruth was torn between wanting to run away and the longing to throw herself into his arms whenever he appeared.

But he called to her to come in and when she opened the door there he was, facing her, smiling. A smile which unexpectedly sent her heart soaring . . .

"You timed yourself well." He smiled, looking at the tray he was holding. "I was just on my way through with the coffee!"

In the sitting-room, he placed the tray on a low table between two armchairs, then leaned across to switch off the television.

"Leave it on . . ." Ruth's voice had a breathless catch in it.

"It's all right," he answered easily. "I'll hear the result of the match later."

IN the centre of the small table sat a carved wooden elephant, one of a pair Stuart had bought from a market stall one afternoon.

He had wanted to give them to her, but laughingly, she had insisted that they each take one. Then, when they were married the elephants would be together again in their new home.

Ruth leaned forward to turn it round in the same instant as Stuart bent to pick up the coffee-pot.

"Why did you do that?" He sounded surprised.

Their faces were almost touching.

Ruth jerked her head back, bright colour flaring into her face.

"Do what?" She sounded flustered, defensive, as if he had made some serious accusation and she was denying all knowledge of the offence.

Stuart stared at Ruth for a long moment, holding her eyes with his, her confusion seeming to trigger off a strange new awareness.

Slowly, he lowered his head. He began to pour the coffee into the mugs, noticing with a slight sense of shock that his hand was unsteady. But when he spoke, his voice was quite normal.

"You turned my elephant round," he said. He waited for her reply, seeming to give all his attention to the coffee.

"He was facing the wrong way," Ruth answered, the corners of her mouth upturning.

"The wrong way for what?" Stuart demanded, frowning slightly.

"For good luck!" Ruth's smile faded as she fought to control a sensation of inexplicable anger. "Everyone knows that elephants must always face the door . . ."

"That's just a superstition." Stuart raised his eyebrows in a mocking way.

"Don't tell me you don't believe in superstition?" Ruth spoke recklessly. "What about falling in love at first sight, for instance?"

Stuart gazed at her in bewilderment and she was goaded into uttering even more rash words.

"What about Moira Dunbar?" The words fell from her lips and were instantly regretted, but it was too late.

Stuart was silent for a moment as he considered his answer.

"Yes, how about Moira Dunbar?" He countered her question with a quiet smile of amusement. "Believe it or not, I bumped into her at lunch-time today."

"So . . . ?" Ruth's gaze was intent, her eyes wide and glittering.

He shrugged carelessly, looking down at his knees, seeming to notice a speck of dust which he flicked away.

"So we had lunch together, the charming Moira and myself." He looked up again. "Any objections?"

Ruth's eyes were hidden from him as she snatched the engagement ring from her finger. She slammed it down on the table.

"None at all," she spoke in a tight, furious tone. "Consider yourself free to have lunch with anyone you want."

O N the way home, Ruth congratulated herself on making such a dignified exit from his flat — and from his life. She was glad, she told herself, glad that she had found out about him in time. As if taking another girl out to lunch was unimportant, she thought angrily.

Her parents were still in the garden when Ruth reached her home. Dry eyed and with careful poise, she told her mother what had taken place.

"So I gave him back his ring, and that's that," she finished quietly.

Aghast, Madge Gilchrist moved closer to her daughter, as if to hug her.

"Oh no, Ruth," she murmured, as tears filled her eyes.

But Ruth was already turning away.

"I'll start preparing the tea." She walked back into the house.

Tears rolled down Madge's cheeks and her husband put his arm round her shoulders, drawing her close to him.

"Don't cry, dearest," he said soothingly. "Maybe it's for the best — better to find him out now than after they're married."

Sombrely, Madge let her head droop against his shoulder.

"It's not that, George, it's just that I don't know how she can be so cool and matter of fact about it."

He led her over to the garden seat and gently pulled off her dirty gardening gloves.

"You don't suit these clumsy things, Madge," he said, tossing them far away. He tenderly kissed her dainty hands, talking to her, making her smile through her tears.

From the kitchen window, Ruth caught a glimpse of them and she hastily looked away. Her parents' open displays of affection didn't usually upset her, but today, for once, Ruth was irritated by the scene.

Anyhow, you'd think they'd grow weary of kissing after all these years! Then with startling suddenness a feeling of utter desolation swept over her. She would never have grown weary of kissing Stuart, she thought bleakly, never in a million years.

She thrust the new and tormenting thought out of her mind as she prepared a salad for tea.

As her parents came into the kitchen there was an awkward silence.

"Well, you've been busy," her father said, briskly. And her mother, equally ill at ease, tried to sound cheerful.

"This all looks delicious, I must say." She smiled gently at her daughter.

The three sat down to eat in a tense atmosphere.

Ruth looked at the food on her plate and she knew that even one mouthful would choke her. Tears began to fall and sobs welled up from her aching heart.

Suddenly, she pushed back her chair and ran from the room, rushing upstairs to throw herself down on her bed, crying bitterly.

MADGE GILCHRIST stood up and walked over to close the kitchen door.

"I don't suppose she really needs an audience," she remarked. "But I do hate to hear her crying."

"Nor me," George made a pretence of eating. "But I'm sure it'll do her a power of good, poor lass."

They lingered on at the tea-table, drinking several cups of tea, at a loss as how best to help their daughter now.

When they heard a knock at the door, Madge continued to sit there, her thoughts forlornly circling around her daughter.

George went to see who was there and re-appeared in the kitchen doorway almost immediately.

"Stuart's here." Mr Gilchrist ushered the young man in, uncertainly. "I've told him Ruth's . . ." He cleared his throat. "I mean I've told him Ruth's upset."

But there was no air of uncertainty about Stuart. In fact, he seemed unusually confident and sure of himself. He smiled at them both.

"I'd still like to see her, please," he announced. Then he looked at Madge directly.

"As a matter of fact, I don't intend to leave until I've spoken to her — unless you throw me out," he added.

Mr Gilchrist took a step towards him.

"And if we do?" he demanded.

Stuart smiled ruefully, suddenly looking young and nervous.

"Then I'll sit on your doorstep until Ruth comes out to me."

The older man's mouth twitched into an answering smile.

"I could shake you by the hand, Stuart!"

"Not yet, George!" His wife snapped the words out, then she looked angrily at Stuart. "My daughter is upstairs crying her eyes out because of you!"

Stuart spread out his hands in a gesture of appeal.

"On my word of honour, Ruth has no reason to be jealous." Then a smile began in his eyes and swept across his features.

"All I want is to tell her that. And I want to let her know that I'm delighted by her jealousy," he admitted.

Mr Gilchrist raised his eyes upwards.

"Better go and find her then, lad."

M ADGE and George looked at each other.

"It's just like I was saying this afternoon," he said. "Do you remember when Robin was born and we didn't realise that Ruth was jealous of the new baby until the day she threw a tantrum to end all tantrums?"

"Did you say that, dear? I don't recall," Mrs Gilchrist answered. "But yes, you're right. Once she got the tantrum over with, she got things more into perspective." She stopped speaking and looked up, although there was no sound from upstairs.

Ruth had fallen asleep. She turned, sleepily confused, as Stuart sat down on the edge of her bed.

But he wasn't looking at her, he was lifting up the elephant from her bedside cabinet.

"Your mate had a bit of bad luck today," he told it very seriously. "He forgot to face the door, and he witnessed a terrible row.

"There was this jealous woman, you see," he went on. "Yes, your friend who lives with me was quite surprised. But me — I was astounded! I didn't even imagine that the lady loved me so much . . ."

"Stuart, you fool." Ruth sat up, leaning on one elbow, smiling at him through eyes which were red and swollen with weeping.

He looked at her at last.

"I love you, Ruth," he said simply, and held out his hand to her.

As her hand reached out towards his, Ruth knew that she would always remember this moment when a gentle clasping of hands brought them together.

It was a moment of exquisite understanding, forging their love into an unforgettable, intimate harmony. □

A Sorrow Shared

by Ailie Scullion

F ROM her farmhouse high on the hill, Janet Cormack could see the town bus wend its way among the foothills, stopping occasionally to drop off a passenger, or pick up a parcel to be delivered to some neighbouring farm. Being far off the main road, Janet seldom made use of this country service.

Her farm was aptly named Hilltop, and Janet had been running it with the aid of hired help for two years now, since the death of her husband, Graeme. Often, she would ask herself if there was any point carrying on? She had several relatives in the city who would have welcomed her back, for she was not country-bred, like Aunt Milly.

Country life had proved absorbing, right from the start. In time, she'd made some lasting friendships. Mostly, however, it had just been the two of them, determined to make a go of Hilltop Farm, and their only real sorrow was that, as yet, there had been no children. Their closest relative had been Aunt Milly. She was Graeme's aunt, really, but Janet had claimed her as her own. She was a tower of strength when Graeme died, and came to stay with Janet for weeks, despite having her own place to run, but then she had to return home.

Janet had always left the pig rearing to her husband — unable to tell him they terrified her. Usually, she had to stand beside the huts and brace herself before going inside. It was their noises that frightened her — the muffled grunts of the adults, and the squeals of the tiny piglets.

There was a man, Aunt Milly told Janet, who had worked for her last summer. Perhaps she could get in touch with him?

That was why, each day, Janet kept an eye open for the town bus as it passed the road at the foot of her hill. Perhaps, soon, the man would arrive, but until then she would just have to carry on alone.

With a sigh she stooped to pick up a bucket filled with meal. Weighed down under the load she set out for the wood.

Only recently, the vet had to be called to Cleo, one of the sows in farrow. After the litter was born, he assured Janet they were all perfectly healthy. Even so, this did little to reassure her.

The piggery had been built in a clearing in the small wood which belonged to Janet's property and was quite impressive. It had been another of Graeme's ideas, because, he told Janet, saddlebacks were good grazers and there was plenty of space there.

The huts were built entirely out of bales of straw, and stood just four feet high with timber supports over the doorway. The outsides were wired with sheep netting and the roof made of thatched hurdles. Such ingenuity, she marvelled, must not be destroyed. There and then she decided she could never sell the herd.

O NCE more the town bus had passed the bottom of her road without stopping, and there was nothing she could do, but carry on with the chores. Even at this distance from the huts, she could hear the sound of the mother and her young family.

Somehow, she had got it into her mind that the sow was in distress, and that there was something wrong with the litter. Not even their huge appetites reassured her. Yet, she knew so little about them, what could she do? Perhaps she would ring the vet again.

It usually took rather a long time to carry the pail of meal up from the farm, and at that precise moment she felt quite breathless. She decided to rest for a while.

In a moment she would carry on, she told herself, but right now, Janet shut her eyes and let the sun warm her bones. When she opened them again a tall man stood a few yards away. Strangely enough, she felt unafraid. He was slender, rather delicate looking, she decided, with fair hair and sad blue eyes.

"I hope I didn't startle you," he began. "I thought you were asleep."

She assured him that she had just been resting.

"You must be Janet Cormack," he decided, then explained, "your aunt sent me."

He had a nice voice, she admitted reluctantly, but didn't resemble a farm worker at all — he was so painfully thin. What on earth had Aunt Milly been thinking about to send such a person?

Now she studied the young man again, then rubbing her hands on her apron, stood up.

"Yes, I'm Janet Cormack," she confirmed almost defensively.

"And I'm Dan Bruce." The stranger smiled at her as he introduced himself and came forward, hand outstretched. She took it unwillingly then felt surprised by the firm grasp.

"I worked for your aunt last summer," he explained now, then added haltingly, "after I came out of hospital."

She might have guessed it. The man was recuperating from some illness. Really, Janet thought with dismay, Aunt Milly's choice had not been suitable.

"I once had a place something like this, over on the east coast." He spoke quietly, as though trying out the words for the very first time.

"Then you know something about pigs, Mr Bruce?" It was almost too incredible to believe.

He nodded.

THE sow had been a black saddleback and the sire a white boar. In the trade, traditionalists would call the offspring blue, but Janet remembered that it had been Graeme's intention to build up an export trade, and it was a strain popular on the Continent.

"A Wessex," Dan said slowly, then rubbed his chin. "The little ones seem to be doing well enough. May I examine them?"

The tiny piglets were housed in a large basket lined with wheat chaff.

When Janet nodded her agreement, Dan crouched beside the litter.

"I was just about to feed them," Janet said hopefully.

"Here, let me," he offered.

The sound of squealing became almost unbearable and Janet backed away, her heart thumping. Dan Bruce looked at her strangely.

"The little ones look fine," he told her, "but need their teeth clipped, I'm thinking. Do you have pincers?"

Her eyes flew to a shelf just above the low doorway.

"Are those what you mean?"

Once more, Dan Bruce looked at her, before lifting down from the shelf, a pair of sharp-looking instruments.

"You're not over fond of pigs."

It was a statement rather than a question, and she nodded.

"What are you going to do?" she enquired anxiously, and Dan Bruce grinned at her.

"It will be quite painless, I assure you. I've done this often."

With a deft movement he prised open the mouth of the small animal and proceeded to nip off the edges of its teeth.

"They are overgrown," he explained as he worked, "and must be causing the sow discomfort when they suckle."

AS they walked back from the woods, Janet remembered something. "How did you get up here, Dan? I did not see anyone come off the bus."

He sent her a sheepish grin.

"I fell asleep and missed my stop. Had to walk a fair bit back."

"Oh dear." She laughed, then said impulsively, "Come up to the house and have a cup of tea."

He appeared to hesitate.

"Your aunt said something about a small cottage," he said tentatively.

Janet noticed his reluctance but went on.

"There is, of course, and it is quite comfortable, but you must come and have a meal before you settle in. Besides, we must talk about wages, etc."

"I think you should know something, Mrs Cormack."

Here it comes, she thought.

"I've had to go into hospital several times over the past six years. Don't worry though, the doctors say I'm perfectly all right now, but I do have to return for check-ups every now and then. Will that be acceptable?"

He was being so honest with her, how could she refuse?

And that was how Dan came to work for Janet. After two months, she realised she'd made the right decision, for, despite his rather delicate appearance, he worked like someone possessed. Fences were mended, as well as the normal work with the livestock, and a stream which had been causing trouble for years was suddenly unblocked.

It was a fine morning when she set off for the wood and Dan's cottage.

Janet was glad he looked better. Gone were the pale cheeks, and instead, he sported a tan.

Comfort

THE right kind of words in sorrow
Are often so hard to say,
But a gentle tone, and a clasping hand
Can help ease the heartache away.
And just being there can mean so much,
When someone feels alone.
And the comfort spread in the strength you give,
Brings a warmth in the kindness shown.

Elizabeth Gozney

"You never come up to the farmhouse for a chat," she accused, then chuckled, "so I guess the mountain must come to Mohammed."

He gazed at her rather sheepishly.

"I'm sorry, I should have come over. I've been trying to get on top of things up here, but I did intend to call. There are a couple of yearlings, Mrs Cormack. Isn't it time you . . ."

She nodded, with a smile.

"Yes, Dan. That's why I'm here, actually. I want you to go to market with me on Thursday."

"To market?" The words came out in a hoarse whisper. "Oh no, Mrs Cormack. I couldn't possibly . . . You will have to find someone else."

She felt stunned by the refusal, yet he did not seem to intend offering any explanation.

That night, she phoned Aunt Milly and they spoke for more than an hour. Afterwards, Janet could have kicked herself for having been so insensitive, but how was she to know?

It was Aunt Milly who put everything into perspective when she explained about the tragedy which had befallen Dan Bruce six years before. He had driven into the neighbouring market town to renew some stock. Whilst away, a fire broke out on his farm and in it, he lost his wife and small child. Afterwards, Dan suffered a complete breakdown, sold up his property and had been in and out of hospitals ever since.

Later, Janet sat down and switched on the television. She could not concentrate on the play showing and was about to switch off when she heard the tap on her door.

Dan Bruce stood, regarding her silently.

"May I come in please, Mrs Cormack . . . Janet. I'd like to talk to you."

She led him through to the living-room and pointed to a comfortable armchair by the fire.

"I've decided to come with you to the market on Thursday, Janet, if you still want me to?

"I've given the matter a great deal of thought, since your visit this afternoon. But perhaps I should explain."

She held up a hand.

"There's no need," she wanted to save him the pain of remembering. "You see I phoned Aunt Milly earlier. She told me all about your trouble."

For a moment a frown played about his brow.

"I wish your aunt had not told you, Janet — I don't want sympathy. That's been my trouble all along. Everyone wants to lighten my burden."

"I wasn't going to offer sympathy, Dan," she said almost curtly. "I just wanted you to know I understood what you had been through. You see, our positions are not dissimilar."

He looked startled.

"Your husband?" he asked slowly and Janet nodded her head.

"I lost him two years ago, Dan. It was one of those stupid accidents which should never have happened. His tractor toppled over in that field behind the wood."

As she spoke, Janet realised it was the first time she had put the fatal incident into words, and as she did so, a cloud seemed to lift from her mind.

"For a while, Dan, I wanted to give up everything, go back to town where I grew up, then . . ." As she paused he leaned forward urgently.

"What was it that made you carry on, Janet?" He was eager to learn.

"This place," she told him simply, "but especially my husband's piggery. This may sound crazy to you for, as you know, I'm terrified of the animals, but it was those funny little huts he built so carefully that made me change my mind. How could I allow anyone to pull them down?"

Dan stood up.

"What time would you like me here on Thursday?" he enquired, and Janet noticed his determination and admired it.

A S you can see, gentlemen," the auctioneer cried, "we have here some very fine saddlebacks. These Wessexes are particularly fine beasts." He touched one with his hawthorn stick.

"You see the head, folk, the long snout and clean-cut jowl. And look at the markings. I'd say these were the finest animals I've sold in years."

Janet felt herself swell with pride. Perhaps she would never conquer her fear of pigs, but today she felt justly proud that Graeme's earlier labours had not been in vain.

It was then she noticed Dan Bruce. He was listening attentively to the bidding and as the price rose sharply he drew nearer to where the auctioneer sat, high on the white painted fence.

"Sold," shouted the man on the fence, "to the gentleman on my right. What did you say your name was, sir?"

On the road home, Janet remained silent for most of the way. At last curiosity got the better of her.

"What on earth possessed you to bid for my pigs, Dan?" she asked.

He grinned across at her.

"I think it was Janie who did it. I couldn't bear to be parted from her."

"Janie?" She let out a yell. "You called her Janie?"

He looked sheepish.

"After you, I'm afraid. She was such a brave one, you see, and kept herself busy all day, bustling about, foraging for food."

"After me, Dan," she echoed. "You called a pig after me?"

They drove into the farmyard and straight up to the front door. Janet led Dan through to the kitchen and put on the kettle. Later, when she placed a plate of stew and potatoes before him, he ate ravenously, then home-made apple pie and cream. She noticed in the past few weeks he'd begun to fill out a bit, and was happy. Then, catching her watching him, Dan smiled and she saw his eyes were bright and clear. They seemed to come alive right before her. When he stretched out his hand and took hers, she did not resist.

"Until I met you, Janet, I was content to dwell in the past, not giving a thought that other folk had problems. But it was when I actually visited the market today, I knew. I had knocked down the last barrier, and was on the home stretch. I shall never look back again, Janet, I promise you."

"You'll stay for a chat?" she asked him confidently, and he nodded. He didn't want to leave the warmth of this home, ever again, and looking at Janet, her face radiant, he knew he would never have to.

Her warm smile seemed to fill the entire kitchen, and he knew with certainty that summer was just around the corner.

"Well, Janet," he told her firmly. "We've shared our sorrows — now let's share our joys." □

The charming East Lothian village of Pencaitland is divided in two by the Tyne Water. A bridge, dating from 1510, connects Wester Pencaitland with its neighbour Easter Pencaitland. Wester Pencaitland has an old mercat cross and Easter Pencaitland is justly proud of its church, the walls of which date from the twelfth century. The aisle is late thirteenth century, the tower is dated 1631, and the pulpit is seventeenth century oak.

PENCAITLAND, MIDLOTHIAN : J CAMPBELL KERR

H

So Near And Yet So Far

I T was a beautiful morning. A lovely light-hearted sort of morning, with sunshine shining all over the Scottish countryside. Yet my heart was heavy as I drove my small car out of Glasgow.

What does a girl do when she has lost her temper with the man she loves, and in a moment of reckless exasperation told him she doesn't want to see him again? What in the world can she do?

Apologise prettily? Tell him: "I'm sorry"? But those two simple words are quite the most difficult to say at times. I knew, for all weekend I had hovered by the phone trying to force myself to call Ian and say them. But all to no avail. For every time I remembered that moment two days ago, I heard my own angry voice.

"I don't want to see you ever again!"

by Christine Maxwell

"Right!" he had replied, equally adamant. "Then let's call it a day!"

If only we had been alone! If only I could have put my arms around his neck and apologised. But in a busy restaurant that couldn't be done. What I did do was to get up from the table where we'd been having lunch and walk straight out of the room.

Now here I was, on this gorgeous day, driving out to the country to keep a promise made to my three little nephews, and feeling more miserable than I had ever done in my life. I wasn't at all in the mood for this Monday half-term school holiday.

With both our parents gone, Margaret was my only close relative, and it was wonderful when she settled within easy reach of where I was working. I had enjoyed my spell of teaching in Glasgow, and with Ian as my guide I had discovered how interesting Glasgow really was.

WELL, I wouldn't stay on in this city, I decided glumly. Not now! But my spirits lifted a little as I stepped out of the car and received a boisterous welcome from the three youngsters awaiting me in the front garden of their pleasant new home. They clustered round, full of welcome for Auntie Linda.

Colin, aged eight, was bright as a button. Eagerly he informed me they were all ready to go out with me. Six-year-old Mark, his small admiring shadow, repeated what Colin had said, while Ronnie, who was three and a bit, hopped about excitedly, indicating his agreement.

What darlings they were, I thought. Their affectionate greeting soothed some of the pain in my heart, yet I couldn't forget what Ian had said about them on Saturday, when we met for that fatal lunch.

"You're taking your nephews out for the day on Monday?" he had queried. "All three? Then you'd better put collars and chains on them!"

"Ian!" I had protested. "They're really well behaved. Remember how good they were when we took them for a run in your car."

"For half an hour!" He had grinned.

I really believe that was what started our argument which developed so disastrously up to the point when he said that I was turning into a 'bossy little school ma'am!' It was then I lost my temper completely . . .

"Auntie," Colin broke into my troubled thoughts. "We know where we want you to take us. Please, can we go to see that lovely museum you told us about. The one with engines and things."

"And with tram-cars," Mark added.

"T'am-ca's!" Ronnie piped up like a small echo.

I gazed back doubtfully. The Museum of Transport in Glasgow was one of the most interesting places I had ever visited with Ian, and sure enough I had told the boys about it next time I saw them. But I didn't want to go back into Glasgow. I had thought of a day in the fresh country air.

"Please, Auntie Linda," Colin coaxed. "And please could we go to Glasgow by train instead of your car? Like Daddy does every day. Look, I've got a pocket in my anorak that's meant for tickets so I could keep them safe for you. There's a zip to keep it shut."

So off we went to the small local station. They behaved like angels all the way into Glasgow, sitting quietly in the train, and pointing out the interesting things they saw through the window.

"Is the museum here?" Colin asked as we arrived in Glasgow's big Central Station.

"Not quite," I told him. "We get another train from here to near the museum. Come on — we'll get more tickets."

WALKING down the slope towards the ticket office, I felt my depression return. To think that barely a stone's throw from these big entrance gates was the office where Ian worked! To think it was possible to walk through these gates, along the street, up some stairs, and ask to see him!

Yes, physically possible, no doubt, but I couldn't have done it. Instead, I bought tickets for Pollokshields East Station, allowing Colin to take charge of them again, as he'd been very careful with the first batch.

"Is it an electric train we go on now?" Colin inquired. "Oh, goody!" he replied when I nodded. "The doors open and shut all by themselves," the knowledgeable child informed his little brothers.

All three decided this sort of train was good fun. They were disappointed to find the journey lasted only four minutes, but left obediently when I told them, and followed me through the ticket office then up the steps towards the street.

Three weeks ago I had walked up these very steps with Ian — so gaily and so light heartedly! Once again I struggled to push such dismal thoughts to one side as we reached the museum.

Anyone who has ever visited the Glasgow Museum of Transport must agree it is a wonderful place, a perfect paradise for small boys. My three stared at the exhibits with eyes wide, hardly able to believe what they saw.

IT was the road-roller that Colin really liked best. Mark fell in love with a wooden wheelbarrow, of all things, and wanted me to buy it for him. I had to explain these things weren't for sale, not even the wheelbarrow, originally used when the first sod was cut on the Deeside railway many years ago.

The trams fascinated little Ronnie. While the other two glued their noses to a glass case containing a model caravan, he made his way up again to the high walkway which ran between the trams.

I had to run after him, to keep him in sight. After watching for a little while I told him it was time to come down. Anxiously, I noticed Colin and Mark had moved away out of sight.

Ronnie shook his head firmly.

"Not go down," he announced, edging away from me.

I picked him up. That was the moment when he stopped being the sweet little nephew who climbed up on one's knee and asked for a kiss. It was almost impossible to hold the defiant, struggling imp he suddenly became. When a small, sturdily-shod foot dealt me a sharp kick on the shins I put him down quickly.

"Ronnie, stop it!" I said in the voice I used to quell unruly pupils at school. "Come and see if we can find Colin and Mark."

"No, don't want to!" Ronnie informed me angrily, taking a firm grip of the railing.

When I prised him away he started to yell. Other people in the museum stared up in surprise, which soon turned to amusement as they watched the contest between us.

By sheer force I got him down to the floor, still bawling at the top of his voice. I dragged him along till I found the other two. They seemed quite unconcerned by their small brother's cries.

"Give him a smack," Colin suggested. "Mummy says when he goes on like that it's just temper."

"Yes, give him a smack," Mark also recommended.

I WAS sorely tempted to throw all my modern views on corporal punishment to the wind and do what they advised.

"Be quiet at once, Ronnie!" I ordered. "If you go on with that noise I'll give you a smacking."

I believe I would have done too! But Ronnie's roars ceased abruptly. It might have been because he had just noticed something else he wanted to inspect. Thankful for quietness again, I followed him and the others to the place where vintage cars were displayed.

"Look at that man sitting in the car." Colin laughed, pointing to a handsome dark blue car with big brass lamps.

It was an Argyll of 1907, and the figure seated in it was a realistic looking man with a bushy moustache, wearing a cloth cap and long coat in the fashion of the day.

"He's got an awful long coat on." Mark chuckled.

"I think he's lonely," Colin remarked. "I'll climb up and sit beside him for a little."

And before I could prevent him, he was over the low blue rail round the cars and up in the front seat of the old car, beaming down at his little brothers.

Colin! My well-behaved eldest nephew! I was shocked.

"Come down at once!" I cried in annoyance.

"I like it up here," was his answer. "Come on, Mark, see if you can get up, too. You could sit in the back seat."

Mark eluded my grasp. But one of the attendants moved into sight. One glimpse of his expression and Colin and Mark were back over the rail, hurrying away to look at the steam engines again.

I followed them swiftly, Ronnie trotting by my side. But by now, all their initial obedience had gone. Ignoring me completely, they dashed here and there. As soon as I caught one, another vanished round a corner.

I must get them out of here, I thought desperately, giving up my plan of lunch in the restaurant here, which I'd previously thought would be a good place for this part of the treat.

No, I wasn't going to risk staying here any longer. We'd take the first available train back to the Central. And then? Dare I take them to a restaurant in town? Suppose they were wild and disobedient there?

"Now, listen to me, boys," I said severely. "You've all been very naughty. If you don't stop it at once, I'll take you straight home without any lunch."

Three pairs of eyes regarded me with surprise. It was obvious they thought Auntie Linda was being unnecessarily cross.

"We'll be good," Colin assured me. "Sorry, Auntie," he added with his most winning smile.

"I'll be good too," Mark declared. "I'm so hungry." He sighed.

Ronnie said nothing. He just gave an angelic smile that would have melted the stoniest heart. I couldn't go on being angry and decided to trust them.

"All right. We'll go for the train then have lunch somewhere," I agreed.

L EAVING the museum, we turned left along Albert Drive. But Mark stopped.

"My shoe's coming off," he complained.

As I wrestled with a knot in his lace, I realised the other two had gone on. Fortunately they paused at the top of the steps which led down to the station. At last Mark's shoe was safely tied again.

"Come along, dear, let's hurry," I urged him, for there was the sound of a train in the station.

Then Colin and Ronnie disappeared. Surely they hadn't gone down on to the platform. But Colin had the tickets and would be allowed to go through. With Mark running beside me, I flew to the steps, then rushed down and through the glass doors. The train was just moving away from the platform and Colin stood there alone.

"Colin, where's Ronnie?" I panted.

Eight-year-old as he was, Colin started to cry.

"He's away in that train, Auntie Linda." He sobbed. "He let go my hand and jumped in with the other people, then the doors shut. He'll get lost," wailed poor Colin.

"Ronnie will be all right," I said shakily. "He'll stay in the train till it gets to the Central."

In four minutes' time? Already one minute was gone. Then in a flash I knew what to do. I'd glimpsed a phone in the ticket office as we passed it on our way in. If I could use it . . .

M Y fingers trembled when I held the receiver, waiting for someone in Ian's office to answer. My voice wasn't steady as I asked to speak to Mr Ian Galbraith. Almost at once I heard his deep voice.

"Ian, it's Linda," I gasped. "I'm at Pollokshields East with the boys and little Ronnie has got on a train by himself. It'll arrive at the Central in just a minute or so. Oh, Ian, please could you dash over and get him? We'll come on the next train —"

I heard the receiver slam down. But not before I also heard what Ian said, very rapidly, as if he had grasped the urgency of the situation.

"Don't worry, darling! I'll go . . ."

Had he really said that? Had he called me darling, in spite of what had happened on Saturday? I forgot my anxiety about Ronnie as a sudden glow of happiness warmed my heart.

Another train arrived at the busy platform. Four minutes later it deposited us at the Central Station, and there at the barrier was Ian, a rather subdued-looking Ronnie beside him.

"Ian, I'm sorry," I whispered. "I didn't mean what I said on Saturday. Please forgive me for everything."

Ian's blue eyes looked directly into mine.

"I'm sorry, too, Linda," he told me. "I shouldn't have criticised you like that. All weekend I've been trying to make myself phone you to apologise, but I was so afraid you'd still be angry."

Just as it had been with me!

WE stood smiling at each other, forgetting the boys. But Mark tugged at my arm.

"Auntie Linda, I'm hungry," he reminded me.

It was Ian who settled that problem.

"What about all of you coming for lunch with me?" he inquired. "It's almost one o'clock so I'm free. I know a place near here that would do."

Three little faces lit up with joy. After the fright they'd all had, the boys were more than ready for food.

"Mato thoup!" Ronnie said eagerly.

"He means he wants tomato soup for his lunch," the ever-helpful Colin explained.

"Then he shall have it!" I promised, gathering Ronnie up in my arms to give him a hug.

The sun was shining brightly outside and somehow it seemed to have filtered into the station itself. As we went together down the slope towards the gates, I knew this dusty noisy old station would always be, to me, the best place in all the world! □

Game, Set — And Match

By Elspeth Rae

WELL, have you made any progress?"
"Did you speak to him?"
"Have you found out his name?"

Nancy Edgar looked at the circle of expectant faces around her desk and shook her head.

"No." She smiled ruefully as she slipped into her seat beside the office window. "Absolutely nothing to report! He was there again, with yet another girl! But they played down at the far end of the courts all night, so I didn't catch his eye once."

"Oh, Nancy!" Auburn-haired Elizabeth Blair stamped her foot in exasperation. "You're going to have to do something — it's been six weeks now. And you haven't even said hello to the boy."

"She's right, Nancy." Tall, quietly-spoken Barbara Gillies put in. "It's the middle of August now. The tennis season will come to an end in September and you might never see him again."

"Oh, don't!" Nancy cried, running a hand through her shining fair hair. "I daren't think about that. I just haven't a clue what to do."

"Dear me, that does sound ominous — perhaps I can help?" The girls wheeled round to find Mrs McLaren, the office supervisor, standing behind them, her eyes twinkling.

"Oh, I don't think so, Mrs McLaren," Nancy murmured, blushing with embarrassment. "It sounds so stupid . . ."

"Try me, anyway," Mrs McLaren invited with a friendly smile.

Before Nancy could explain, though, Elizabeth Blair chimed in. "The problem is that our Nancy's fallen head over heels in love, Mrs McLaren! With a young man she sees down at her local tennis courts. Only, since she's never spoken to him, he doesn't know she exists. So it looks as if it's going to be a sad case of unrequited love."

THERE, I said it would sound ridiculous!" Nancy exclaimed. "You must think I'm crazy, Mrs McLaren."

"Not a bit, dear!" Mrs McLaren perched on the edge of Nancy's desk, smiling reflectively. "You'll never believe

this, Nancy, but I had the very same problem when my husband first appeared on my horizon. That was down at the ice-rink, though, not at the tennis courts. The lengths I went to get to know my Bob!''

"And how did you manage it in the end, Mrs McLaren?" Barbara Gillies asked curiously.

"Well, it might sound very odd." The older woman chuckled. "I started going to the rink with another lad! As a matter of fact, it was my cousin, Frank, but Bob didn't know that!

"Young men like competition, you know." She smiled at the girls.

"So when Bob saw me smiling at him, he took a second look then decided he was going to try to lure me away from my Frank."

"So what happened?" Nancy asked eagerly.

"Oh, as soon as Bob and I got talking, that was it!" Mrs McLaren replied. "He was as keen on me as I was on him, and we never looked back."

Then, looking up at the clock, she clapped her hands in dismay.

"Ten past nine!" she exclaimed. "And not a single ledger out. Come on, girls, we'll have to do better than this!"

I T was six o'clock when Nancy eventually arrived home that Thursday, hot and rumpled after an uncomfortable bus ride from the city.

Her brother Scott poked his head out of the kitchen as Nancy started upstairs.

"Nick's here for tea," he announced, "so I'm making sausages and chips for us and Dad. Do you want some, Sis?"

"No thanks, love. I'll have a salad," Nancy replied with a smile, as she went into the bathroom to wash and change.

Nick Collins had been Scott's closest friend for three years now, ever since the Edgars had moved into the district. He must have eaten hundreds of meals with them, which meant yards of sausages and mountains of chips. That was usually Nick's suggestion when he was asked what he would like to eat.

L ATER, over their meal, Norman Edgar looked across at his daughter and winked.

"I don't know what Nick's going to do with himself when our Scott goes off to run his Boys' Brigade camp tomorrow," he said. "He'll have no-one to help him pull his car engine to pieces, or to listen to his latest records."

"I know," Nick nodded his red head in agreement. "Mum's planning all sorts of awful jobs to keep me occupied. I'll have to think of somewhere to escape to."

"You can always go down to the tennis-courts with Nancy," Scott suggested, his dark eyes twinkling.

"Yes!" Nancy's delighted assent made the others stare at her in surprise.

"Oh, will you, Nick?" she pleaded. "Just while Scott's away for this next fortnight! You'd be doing me a real favour."

"But I can't play tennis, Nancy," Nick protested, his grey eyes wide. "Football's my game. I've never held a racquet in my life."

"That doesn't matter," Nancy assured him. "I'll teach you. I just want you to be there with me, Nick. Oh, go on!" she coaxed. "Be a sport!"

"Yes, go on, Nick," Mr Edgar urged laughingly. "It's bound to be better than painting the garden fence, or cutting the lawn."

"I don't know," Scott put in, regarding his sister with narrowing eyes. "It sounds very fishy to me, Nick! I should be careful, if I were you."

"Honestly! All I want is a male escort for a change . . ." Nancy was beginning.

But Nick had already held up his hands in mock surrender. "All right, I'll come quietly," he declared. "When do these tennis lessons begin, then?"

"Tomorrow evening?" Nancy suggested. "If you come round about seven we could go down in your car, Nick."

THE tennis courts where Nancy played were in the local park. They ran the whole length of a high hedge, and the pavilion and booking office were just inside the park gates.

It had been six weeks ago this Thursday evening, when Nancy, standing alone in front of the pavilion, had become aware of someone staring at her.

She had glanced across to find a young man propped up on one elbow on the grass, studying her intently.

Nancy had never seen him before. His thick chestnut hair flopped over his brow, and he had the most penetrating blue eyes she'd ever seen. As their glances had met, she experienced a series of bewildering sensations — her heart had started pounding, her mouth had gone dry and her legs trembly.

Just as she had been about to smile, a blonde girl had come running through the park gates and across the grass to join the young man.

Picking up his sports hold-all, he had jumped to his feet and gone off with the girl to the tennis court.

It was the first time in her nineteen years that Nancy had found herself so attracted to a boy. Previously she had looked on with tolerant amusement when her friends became starry eyed about young men.

Although she had had passing friendships with a few boys, whenever things had looked like becoming serious Nancy had given the boy up.

"I just can't seem to feel deeply about anyone," she had explained to Barbara in the office. "So it's no good pretending." But now, at last, there was no need to pretend, for she had been finally smitten with the love-bug!

She had an idea that his name was Fergus, for she thought she had heard one of his friends call him that one evening. His age? Well, he looked around the same age as Scott and Nick and they were in their early twenties. And what did he work at? Where did he live? The questions had buzzed around in her head.

O H, look! There's Fergus Corner," Nick said, with a wide grin. Nancy, sitting on the grass beside Nick Collins, swung round sharply as the young man spoke. She couldn't believe her eyes, or her ears. But there was no mistaking the athletic-looking figure striding past them up the grassy slope.

Fergus turned as he heard his name, his blue eyes lighting up with recognition as he saw Nick. He raised a hand in greeting before disappearing into the booking office.

"You know him, do you?" Nancy's voice was peculiarly croaky as she turned to her red-haired companion. She had been hoping for a bit of luck, but this was even better than she had anticipated.

"He was at Hightown Comprehensive with me. We were in the same biology class at one point, but not for long. Fergus was one of the brainy ones." Nick smiled ruefully. "He's at university now, I believe, studying medicine."

"And . . ." But Nancy's next question was cut short by the shrilling of the whistle that told them their court was free.

As he had predicted, though, Nick was properly at sea for the first half-hour, and Nancy was chasing all over the courts after wildly-aimed balls. But she was enjoying herself.

At one point she saw the smiling faces of two of her girl friends watching their game through the wire fence.

"Don't you two laugh!" Nancy whispered. "You were just as bad when you started!"

Little Diane Taylor's dark eyes widened in amazement.

"We weren't laughing at him, Nancy," she protested indignantly. "We were admiring him! He's super, Nancy. Wherever did you find him?"

"Who? Nick!" Nancy exclaimed, turning to look over at Scott's friend. "Gosh, he's almost one of the family." As she started back to their court, she smiled to herself.

Nick did look rather striking tonight in his white tee-shirt with that thatch of red hair and his broad shoulders. And that was all to the good, she crowed inwardly.

If Mrs McLaren were to be believed, that was just what was needed to attract Fergus Corner's eye.

T HEY weren't to see much of Fergus that night, because he was with three other young men, all first-class players, down at the far end of the courts.

Nick, having a drink with Nancy before they went home, narrowed his eyes as he watched the four of them. Even from a distance the high standard of their play was obvious.

"Fergus was always terrific at sport," he commented. "I really used to envy him at school. He had everything — brains — muscles — girlfriends galore . . ."

"And poor Nick had nothing, I suppose?" Nancy teased, giving him a playful nudge.

"Well, not much, according to my dad," Nick murmured. And

glancing at him curiously she saw that his grey eyes were unusually solemn.

"I'm afraid I was a bit of a disappointment," he went on. "The only boy coming after three girls. They were expecting great things of me."

"And just what's wrong with you?" she asked indignantly.

Nick burst out laughing.

"Well, I wasn't a great success at school for a start!" he exclaimed. "All I was ever interested in was how car engines worked!"

"But you've got a good job in a garage, what's wrong with that?" she demanded.

"A lot, by Dad's way of thinking." Nick sighed. "In fact," he went on in a sudden burst of confidence, "I had a real inferiority complex, Nancy, until I met your Scott, and became friendly with you and your dad.

"You Edgars have quite different values from my folk. Knowing you all has done a lot for me," he finished shyly.

During the days ahead, though, all Nancy's high hopes were to be dashed. For Fergus didn't put in a single appearance at the courts. She thought he must be on holiday.

MESSAGE OF FAITH

I STOOD outside a Church, before a stained glass window.

The sun but showed the city's grime on untransparent glass, and a maze of leaded panes concealed the Christ they bore.

Then I went inside the Church; saw the window from within.

The sun set free the hues imprisoned in the glass, and I saw a shining Christ, in robes of sparkling blue and a radiance round His head.

See Christ from within the walls of faith. The light of God shines through His mortal flesh as the sun through a stained glass window.

Fadeless as the colours fused in glass, ever shines the glory of the Son of God.

Rev. T. R. S. Campbell

Mrs McLaren and the girls in the office had been jubilant at the initial success of their scheme. Now they couldn't believe the girl's bad luck.

"Never mind," she said, the following Friday lunchtime. "At least I've given Nick a new interest. He's really caught tennis fever now."

"Well, I shouldn't think you'll have any tennis tonight, dear," Mrs McLaren remarked, glancing out of the window. "The rain's not very far away."

In fact, the rain did hold off, so Nancy and Nick went down to the courts as usual. Then, when they were midway between the car park and the pavilion, the heavens opened,

"Run!" Nick yelled, grabbing her by the hand. As they arrived breathlessly at the foot of the pavilion steps, they almost collided with another couple.

Nancy, looking up into a pair of laughing blue eyes, heard Nick say cheerfully, "Hi, Fergus." Somehow she managed to propel her cotton-wool legs up the steps.

"We four seem to have been the only optimistic ones." Fergus laughed. "We have the courts to ourselves."

Nancy had time to register the fact that Fergus had acquired a suntan during his absence, then introductions were being made.

It was the pretty blonde who was with him this evening. Her name was Rosalie Millar and Nancy saw her looking at Nick with admiring eyes.

It was Nick who suggested they might all go along to the corner café, and Nancy could have hugged him for it.

By the time they finally left Fergus and Rosalie to go home in Nick's car, she was floating on a cloud of thistledown.

"How do you like Fergus?" Nick asked quietly.

"Very much," she replied frankly. "Rosalie seems a pleasant girl, too."

"Fergus suggested we might play a mixed doubles with them tomorrow evening, if it's dry," Nick said hesitantly.

"Oh, I'd enjoy that," Nancy said quickly.

"But my tennis isn't up to his standard," Nick protested.

"Your tennis is fine!" she told him firmly. "You play surprisingly well for a beginner, believe me."

By the following Thursday evening Nancy felt she was well on her way to having her dreams realised. All week Fergus Corner had made sure that he spent most of his time at the courts in their company, no matter who he arrived with. And there had been no mistaking the expression in his eyes as he smiled at Nancy. Or the warm touch of his fingers brushing hers as he handed her a tennis ball.

On their visits to the café after tennis, she had listened with interest and amusement as Nick and Fergus had reminisced about their schooldays.

O N Thursday evening, after five dry days, the rain returned suddenly to stop play early. The result was that the café was unusually crowded when the four of them got there.

"Come on, Nancy," Fergus murmured, gripping her arm quickly as they entered. "There's a table for two in the corner, let's grab it."

"But what about Nick and Rosalie?" she asked anxiously, as she found herself manoeuvred into a corner seat.

"They'll be all right," he told her. "They can look after themselves." He smiled, and the expression in his eyes made her forget her misgivings.

Sure enough, a few minutes later, she saw that the other two had found a table by the door.

This was the first time that Nancy and Fergus had been alone together, and much as she had longed for this moment, Nancy might well have felt shy. But he was a fluent and entertaining fellow.

As she sipped her coffee Nancy heard all about his recent week on the Norfolk Broads with his two friends. He told her about the mishaps, the late-night parties, the midnight bathing sessions. And his term-time activities at university seemed equally hilarious.

"How do you fancy coming on to a disco with me this evening, Nancy?" he suddenly asked, reaching over to grip her fingers for a moment with his own. "It's very informal. We can just go as we are."

"Oh, but I can't just go off and leave Nick." She turned to glance across at the red-haired young man.

"Why not?" Fergus chuckled. "He'll get over you."

"Get over me?" Nancy's brow wrinkled in bewilderment.

"Sure!" Fergus said easily. "He thinks you're pretty wonderful, he's told me so."

"He has?" she sipped her coffee slowly, her eyes two dark pools of consternation. He nodded.

"But Rosalie will soon take him in hand," he said wryly. "I've been watching her. She can charm the birds off the trees, that young lady! Nick will fall for her like all the others."

"And then what?" Nancy asked with a slight frown, placing her cup back abruptly on its saucer.

"Then she'll move on to her next conquest, I suppose."

NANCY turned again to look at Nick. He was listening intently to what Rosalie was saying, chin propped on his hand.

Without warning a great wave of emotion swept through her, making her catch her breath.

That girl wasn't going to hurt Nick! No-one was going to hurt him. He was generous, warm hearted and good natured, and such fun to be with. She had learned so many unexpected and lovable things about him during these past two weeks . . .

Nancy turned back to Fergus and it was as though a veil was lifted suddenly from her eyes. He was looking at her questioningly — a pleasant, very charming young man.

Good company, undoubtedly handsome, but a stranger still. He wasn't her sort of person at all — not like Nick.

"Fergus," Nancy said softly. "I've enjoyed the chat and the coffee, but I'm going home now, with Nick. I hope you understand."

He looked at her blankly for a moment, then he gave a sigh and a reluctant smile touched his lips.

"Yes, I understand, Nancy," he said at last. "No hard feelings. I only hope old Nick, there, appreciates his good luck."

Nick did. Fergus could see that, so could Rosalie Millar, and anyone else in the café who chanced to be watching.

Nancy went over to Nick and put her arm around the red-haired lad's shoulders. "Are you coming home now, Nick?" she whispered.

As they went outside the café and walked slowly along the glistening pavement towards the car, arms entwined, Nancy stopped suddenly to look up at her boyfriend.

"Oh, gosh, Nick!" she exclaimed. "Whatever are we going to say to Scott?"

"We could always ask him to be our best man," Nick replied, stooping to kiss her tenderly on the lips. □

If You Ever Need Me...

I N the kitchenette to which they had been banished, the twins were holding yet another council of war — a ceremony that usually followed them having been told off by their mother for some misdemeanour or other. Regrettably, it was happening a little too often for Annette's peace of mind.

Benjy's voice, slightly higher than Paul's, came piping through to the dining-room.

"'S not fair. You started it."

"Didn't." Paul's retort was emphatic, though not particularly indignant. Of the two, he accepted punishment with more resignation.

"Well, Gran lets us do it." Benjy said, indignantly. "Why doesn't she?"

"*She* is the cat's mother." Paul was plainly quoting from an unimpeachable source, but not troubling himself to answer his brother's question.

In the dining-room their parents exchanged glances. Victor, who had arrived late on the scene, sighed patiently.

"What have they been up to this time?"

Setting his favourite roast and potatoes before him, Annette tried to control the growing feeling of irritation. It had been a trying day and the oppressive weather combined with a pregnancy of eight months left her with a feeling of cumbersome lethargy.

She was well aware her temper was on the short side nowadays and the boys, full of life and unending ingenuity when it came to thinking up new mischief, tried it sorely at times.

"The usual catalogue." She made a determined effort to keep her voice light, knowing how he worried when she became depressed or over-tired.

"I'm afraid they got in among your paint pots in the shed, when my back was turned. I didn't have time to clean up either them or the shed, so I told them they'd to stay in the kitchen till you had your dinner."

"Oh dear." Victor's brow was creased momentarily. "What about their meal, the wee rascals?"

"Oh, I managed to wipe the paint off their hands and their mouths. I gave up when it came to their clothes and their hair. No need to worry about them starving, Vic. They're tucking in heartily, in between discussing their opinion of me."

by Jean McDougall

"I'll see to them afterwards," he promised, grinning. The shed could be tidied up later, and probably the boys could be wiped with turps. substitute and turned out good as new. In fact, of late he had taken over the job of bathing them and getting them ready for bed to give his wife more time to herself in the evenings. Usually a good time was had by all.

"What kind of day have *you* had?" she enquired.

"Oh, busy as usual. We've been installing a number of new lifts out of town and it means tearing round as many as possible to do the testing and make sure they're safe and working satisfactorily."

He had been with the same installation firm for some years now and obviously enjoyed the job, though sometimes he wished he had the kind of nine-to-five position that might have let him nip home for lunch during the day — it would have made it a little easier for Annette.

Well, one couldn't have everything. Besides, he felt certain once the baby arrived, Annette would be back to her old serene self, well able to cope with their boisterous offspring.

"I'll take dessert through to our holy terrors," he said with a smile.

TWO small faces surmounted by tumbling curls beamed as he strode through. "Daddy! Daddy!" the boys cried excitedly.

He saw at once his wife hadn't been exaggerating about the paint stains. There were streaks of purple in the golden curls and Paul's face in particular was like a Red Indian's plus war paint.

"Good grief!" Victor stared at them in amazement, part of it real, most of it simulated. "What are you two ruffians doing in my house? Who are you?"

The broad smiles wavered slightly. As usual, the twins exchanged looks for guidance and support.

"I'm Paul," said his elder son.

"We live here," Benjy added, a little concerned.

"You could have fooled me," remarked their father, setting fruit and ice-cream before them. "What have you been doing to my shed and my paint, to say nothing of my brushes?"

"We wanted to help," Benjy said with a sweet smile which was possibly due to the fact that ice-cream was easily his most favourite dessert.

"Well, that kind of help I can do without. And because it's going to take that much longer to get you two cleaned and ready for bed, there won't be so much time for the story, will there?"

The two small boys exchanged disappointed looks.

"What did you mean when you said Gran lets you do it?" he asked curiously.

There was a moment's silence, broken eventually by Paul.

"When we went to stay with her, she let us paint whatever we liked," he muttered.

"All kinds of colours, Dad," Benjy put in excitedly, "green, purple, red . . ."

"OK." Victor held up a hand to stop the inventory. He was well aware of his sons' habit of embroidering the facts.

"Just what did Gran allow you to paint?" he asked carefully.

"Books," the boys said together, triumphantly. "Do you want to see them, Dad? Will we go and get them to show you?"

"You will not." Victor tried hard not to show his relief that the two boys hadn't run riot in their granny's house.

"You'll stay here at the table, finish your meal, and wait till I come back to take that paint off. And you will both promise me never to go in the shed again without permission; and never, never to open a tin of paint unless your mother or I say you can. Is that clear?" He tried to sound suitably stern.

WHEN he got back to the dining-room, carefully carrying a tray with biscuits and coffee, he met his wife's eyes with a rueful grin.

"You're right, love. They are in a mess, but it's partly my fault. I ought to have made sure these tins were well out of their reach. Mind you, I don't know how they managed to prise the lids off but I suppose it serves me right for leaving a couple of screwdrivers lying about. I've warned them I'll have their hides off if they as much as show their noses in that shed again."

Annette visibly relaxed. "I was afraid you'd think I was being too hard on them," she told him. "Sometimes you think I am, don't you?"

"Hey, come on, now. Don't talk like that. I know they must be a bit of a trial to you these days, but they're simply normal boys with surplus energy and it's got to find an outlet somewhere. Wouldn't you like my mother to take them for a little while again to give you a break?"

"No." The word shot out like a bullet and she flushed under his surprised look.

"I mean, your mother has plenty to do with her own affairs — the Guild, the District Council meetings, and all the rest of it. It would be imposing."

"It wouldn't be imposing," he said slowly, pouring coffee into their cups. "You know she loves having them, and the meetings are off till the new session takes up in the autumn. She's said often enough she's always happy to lend a hand — especially with things as they are right now."

"I can cope," she said shortly and the subject was dropped in favour of something less controversial. Later, while her husband scrubbed off paint and deposited the boys in steaming baths, she washed up in the empty kitchen and thought about her mother-in-law.

PRISCILLA MORTON was a pleasant woman who had welcomed her right from the start, first as Victor's special girlfriend and later as a daughter-in-law, always ready to lend a hand whenever necessary or act as baby-sitter whenever the young people felt like having an evening out together.

Annette had appreciated her welcoming attitude and all the friendly helpfulness shown later, but Mrs Morton seemed so capable in every direction, it seemed only natural she took charge at times and her ultra-efficiency tended to make Annette feel inadequate.

The last time the twins had stayed with her over a weekend, they'd returned more unruly than ever, claiming that Gran let them do this and that, so why couldn't they do the same things at home?

"They're playing you up, love." Her husband had grinned when he heard about the claims. "Kids do it the world over. They know they can't get away with playing you up against me, or vice versa, but they can more or less say what they like, about what Gran lets them do in her house."

But Annette had doubts. Sometimes she felt that Mrs Morton tended to spoil her grandsons — forever planning little treats for them like visits to the zoo or a pantomime.

But these were all perfectly natural pursuits for a grandmother and her grandsons, as Victor had pointed out.

However, the boys often returned from these treats over-excited and sometimes sick from the ice-cream and crisps consumed during the day.

The thought made her feel queasy herself as she wiped the last piece of cutlery and deposited it in the drawer. It had not been an easy pregnancy this time.

Of course, she'd been younger then, she reminded herself. Now she seemed to be always anxious about something. And it made her irritable and snappy, impatient with the ones she loved best. These days she felt so fed up with things, and herself most of all. Unbidden, tears rose to her eyes, as they did so often, nowadays.

An arm round her waist brought strength and comfort.

"Mission accomplished," Victor informed her. "Most of the paint's off and our two scamps are fast asleep. What would you do without me?"

"Oh, Vic." For a moment she clung to him, devastated by the thought of ever having to do without his loving kindness and cheerfulness.

"I'm such a wet blanket these days. I'm surprised you're not completely fed up with me."

"I enjoy suffering," he joked. "Come and watch the late movie. I saw the trailer last night and it's a family story — just the type you enjoy, dear."

It was, and she did, but beforehand, she tiptoed upstairs to where her two small boys slept, her heart melting as it always did at the sight of their angelic faces. Her conscience stabbed her at the thought that perhaps sometimes she really was a bit hard on them. She promised herself she'd be more patient the next day.

"Cheer up, it may never happen," Victor greeted her sombre expression when she returned to the sitting-room. "Everything OK upstairs?"

"Oh, yes," she reassured him. "They're sleeping like angels."

The Winner

IT'S very hard to get him
  To tidy his own room —
The thought of straightening his bed,
  Fills him full of gloom!
He never polishes his shoes,
  And leaves the bathroom cluttered;
And lots of things I'd like to say,
  I have to leave unuttered!
"There she goes again," he cries,
  And the battle scarce begun —
He throws his arms around my neck,
  And his mother's heart is won!

Miriam Eker

"Mother phoned when you were upstairs," Vic told her. "She wondered if you'd like a run down to the seaside tomorrow. Largs, maybe, or further afield, if you like."

"Oh. That was kind of her." Annette was grateful. "What did you say?"

"I suggested she check with you on the phone in the morning. Said you were feeling a bit tired tonight and would probably say no."

"Vic!" she rebuked him. "You didn't say it like that, I hope."

"No, love," he laughed. "I was very diplomatic and suitably grateful." He was serious for a moment. "She really means well, you know."

"Oh, I know. She's kind and considerate and so good with the boys." Annette meant every word.

But the thought of a day with Mrs Morton weighed heavily on her mind till the film managed to absorb her. At the end of it, she knew she herself would turn down her mother-in-law's invitation, but, of course, the boys would love to go.

"At least, it'll take their minds of the paint shed," Victor joked.

"I'm supposed to be overseeing an installation in Carlisle tomorrow, Annette, so the chances are I may be late back in the evening," he informed her.

"Maybe it would be a good idea for you to go along on the trip to the seaside. Anyway, see how you're feeling in the morning."

NEXT day was hot and sticky with the promise of higher temperatures, but when Mrs Morton phoned, Annette had already made up her mind.

Priscilla took the refusal very well.

"Of course, my dear, I realise a longish car trip can be a bit uncomfortable for you right now. Will you be all right in the house on your own? Victor mentioned he might be late back from a special job."

"Yes, perfectly." Annette smiled. "The boys are really looking forward to going to the seaside. It's awfully kind of you."

"Oh, you're doing me the favour, letting me borrow them for a while," Priscilla said, cheerfully. "When shall I drop by?"

When she arrived Annette had some coffee ready. The boys had been on their very best behaviour, ready for at least an hour before, and whooped with excitement when the small red car edged its way to their gate.

"Gran! Gran! We painted the shed yesterday. Mum didn't like it, and Dad said he'd take our hides off if we went there again." Their voices sounded almost proud. And Annette shook her head, in pretended dismay.

"I'm not surprised." Mrs Morton with an arm round each smiled at their mother. "You're looking well, Annette. Cool and lovely."

"Thank you. How are you today?" What a kind woman she was, Annette thought guiltily.

Priscilla Morton was blessed with vigorous good health and certainly did not look anywhere near her fifty-odd years. Her skin was as soft and clear as a girl's and her dark hair, streaked with silver, was beautifully styled and shone in the brilliant sunshine. She was also, to Annette's eyes, enviably slim.

"Very fit, thanks," the older woman replied. "Now, is there anything I can do for you before we head for the coast?"

"Not really — but do stay for some coffee, won't you?"

She had her work cut out convincing the older woman that the unwashed dishes in the scullery would give her something to do when she was alone in the afternoon and that Kate, her next-door neighbour was collecting some shopping for her, so no, there was nothing more Mrs Morton could do.

"Well, if you're quite sure," her mother-in-law continued. "And you really have decided not to come with us, have you?"

"I think I'd find it rather hot in the car — it looks as though today's going to be another roaster. But thanks all the same, Gran. It's good of you to take the boys to the sands."

"You know I enjoy it." The older woman laughed.

After the cups had been refilled and drunk, and the twins kissed and directed to be on their best behaviour, the little party piled into Mrs Morton's car. Annette returned the boys' waves as the car moved out of sight, around the corner of the street.

THE next hour passed quickly enough as she coped with the daily chores.

But when everything was shipshape, she was at a loose end and a great feeling of loneliness swept through her. Surely it had been churlish to turn down Mrs Morton's invitation to spend a day at the coast.

If only there was the prospect of Victor getting home early, but he had warned her he'd be late since he was having to visit several sites to check on lift installation safety measures.

Wandering into the garden to sit under the tree's welcome shade, she seemed to be the only one in the avenue with time on her hands.

When she tried to concentrate on a magazine, she felt her eyes closing as though she hadn't slept for nights on end. When she drifted back to consciousness, she heard the soft strains of a transistor and realised Kate must be back, for her neighbour simply had to have music wherever she went.

"Hi, there!" Kate's impish face with its helmet of shiny black hair was smiling through a gap in the hedge. "Some people have it made, I must say."

"Oh, Kate, don't rub it in." She laughed. "I'm already feeling a useless, lazy lump."

"Well, you don't look it, Annette." Kate said, firmly. "You look delightfully cool and beautifully relaxed. That sleep has done you a world of good, and at least, you don't have to worry what the terrible twins are up to. How about us sharing some lunch?"

"Sounds great," Annette replied. "How did the shopping go?"

"Much the same as always, with the usual high prices." The girl sighed. "When will it ever end?"

Annette was astonished to discover she had been asleep for over an hour. By now, the boys and their gran would have reached Largs and be heading for the nearest restaurant, since all three had healthy appetites.

Since she hadn't been very hungry lately, she especially enjoyed the dainty salad Kate had prepared, washed down by lemon tea.

AFTERWARDS, she insisted on clearing up, for on Thursday afternoons, Kate always hurried off to visit her sister who was a long-term patient in a local hospital.

"I made some meringues," Annette said, pressing the box into her friend's shopper. "Even if your sister doesn't feel up to eating them, the nurses will probably use them up at their tea break.

"You get away, Kate, and leave me to wash and tidy up." she said, waving aside her friend's thanks. "I'll leave the table set for you and Joe coming home at six."

Then she was alone again, and after the chores were finished, she made her way back to her own house, trying to decide how best to fill in the rest of the afternoon. There was the layette to be checked over, and the beautiful lacy shawl which her mother had sent was lying on top, in pride of place, to be stroked and admired daily till it could come into its own.

Remembering that today there was a record request programme on the radio she switched on prepared to enjoy some old familiar, dearly loved tunes.

Instead, within minutes the local station was putting out an "on-the-hour" news bulletin. At first, she barely heard the announcement. Then when it sank in, her blood seemed to turn to ice.

An accident . . . a jammed lift . . . engineers trapped many floors up . . . Names not being released yet till relatives informed.

As soon as Carlisle was mentioned Annette knew that Victor had to be involved.

She was petrified at the thought that he could be in danger and she was powerless to help. She really was on her own this time, no Kate next door, no Gran Morton.

Sinking down on the bed, still grasping the baby shawl, she made the effort to clear her head. First and foremost, she must put through a call to Victor's firm. They at least would know the facts.

A girl's rather scared voice at the other end seemed reluctant to part with any information.

SURELY you can put me on to someone who can tell me what has happened. Isn't Mr Cameron or Mr Stewart in?"

There was no one. The girl was simply manning the phones while everyone in authority was out on the various jobs.

"Well, will you please telephone this number the minute you have any information," Annette said sharply. "Meantime, have you the number of the firm in Carlisle which my husband was visiting today?"

After some delay, the telephonist finally produced a number, but it did little for Annette's peace of mind, since each time she tried it, all that could be heard was the exasperating engaged tone.

With all her heart she wished Priscilla Morton could be reached at the end of some telephone. Not once in her entire married life had she ever dreamed of such a thing, but at least with Gran back and the boys looked after, she would be free to drive to Carlisle, and be on the spot for the moment when Victor was brought down to safety.

Resolutely she refused to let her mind dwell on the possibility of some disastrous accident. It was bad enough to be marooned in a faulty lift, but supposing . . . supposing . . .

Desperately she willed the clock to go faster. The boys couldn't be back till teatime at the earliest and Kate usually arrived around five. Supposing she left a note for Kate and then managed to hire a car to take

135

her to Carlisle? But then, it would be a terrible shock for Priscilla to learn about Vic's accident through a third party. And anyway where was she likely to get a car at such short notice? She didn't drive so she'd need someone to take her south.

She could have wept when the Carlisle number still returned the engaged signal. Of course, they would be snowed under by calls.

As calmly as she could she got herself ready for the journey, packing a small overnight bag, just in case. When Kate arrived back she could get away somehow. She knew she would never rest till she was near to Vic. She had to be there, to feel she was giving him some sort of support, however inadequate.

None of the private hire firms could accommodate her. If she had been a driver, they could have offered a car, but otherwise, no. Taxis seemed to be in equally short supply. Of course, it was the height of the holiday season and taxis were at a premium, transporting folk to and from the stations and the airport.

The only other alternative was a train. In her present condition they always made her feel queasy, but right now that just wasn't important. Restlessly she paced back and forth to the front windows looking for Kate's welcome little figure.

Then, incredibly she glimpsed Priscilla's car, several hours before it was due back.

Wordlessly she raced down the garden path, to give quick hugs to the boys, and meeting the older woman's eyes, she knew Victor's mother had already heard the news.

"I was afraid you might have gone on ahead," Priscilla Morton said quietly, steering them into the house. "I tried your number but it was solidly engaged."

After a quick explanation, Annette stammered, "If only Kate would come now, then maybe you would run me to the station, Gran."

"I'll do better than that, lass. I'm going to take you there in the car. Now, let's just keep as calm as we can, for the children's sake, and wait patiently for your neighbour returning."

For the first time in her life, Annette was not only glad to have someone like her mother-in-law take charge, but returned thanks for the clear-headed way the older woman coped with everything. How on earth could she have been so small-minded in the past to resent her efficiency or bridle inwardly because she did things so much more competently than herself?

O N the way south, they tuned in to as many radio news broadcasts as possible, Annette fearful that the next one could relay some dreadful news. If Mrs Morton had any such fears, she kept them hidden behind a mask of calmness, but each broadcast was listened to with grave concentration.

Annette's heart turned over when they reached the address given, to find an ambulance parked at the gates. An official at the front door barred their way till Mrs Morton explained who they were. Then they were shepherded with much kindness to a staff rest room, and there, incredibly, was Victor, oil-streaked and with some bruises, getting up to greet them.

"You two are a sight for sore eyes." He joked. "I've been down safely for the past half hour and trying to get through to the house. Then luckily, I tried Kate's number and she told me the boys were staying overnight with them. I might have known you two would come hot-footing it here."

He enfolded them both in a bear's hug.

"You all right, Annette? I was worried in case this would upset you."

"She has everything under control," his mother told him proudly, grinning at her daughter-in-law. "Now what are you doing, Victor? Are you coming back with us in the car or do you have to stay here?"

"I'm coming home," he said simply, looking at his wife tenderly.

"The ambulance," Annette said then, remembering. "Was someone hurt?"

"No, love, it was just a precaution," he answered.

"Come along," Mrs Morton said, briskly. "I'm sure we all want to get back home as soon as possible." Annette caught her mother-in-law's eye and the two women exchanged understanding looks.

As Priscilla turned away and bustled off towards the car, Annette felt a great surge of affection for her. Never again would she resent Priscilla's efficiency.

Happily Vic and she followed Priscilla, neither saying a word, just glad to be together. Annette was the first to break the silence.

"If the baby's a girl," she whispered to her husband, "don't you think Priscilla would be a lovely name?"

"Priscilla Morton, the second." He stopped walking and took Annette in his arms.

"Whatever you say will be fine with me," he whispered back, then, turning his head to watch his mother walking ahead, added, "But I know someone who'll be very pleased indeed!" □

Then Cupid Stepped In

by BARBARA COWAN

H ILDA MCALLISTER clambered on to the northbound train and as the door was slammed behind her the train started to move slowly from the station.

She stood panting for a moment, clutching the back of a seat to regain her breath, then flopped on to the only available aisle seat after stowing away her parcels and case. Resting her head on the back of the seat for a moment, Hilda closed her eyes thankfully.

It had been quite a week, she mused. She had been looking after her baby nephew and two-year-old niece, while her sister had snatched a few days' holiday with her husband.

When Hilda had settled down for the journey, she brought out a half-knitted matinée jacket. She'd thought she would get it finished while looking after the two little ones, but she should have known better! She'd had enough experience looking after the children of her four older half-brothers and sisters, after all.

It crossed her mind that very few unmarried women would know so much about feeding, winding, and teething as she did. The thought made her smile, before she pulled herself up with a start. The young man sitting beside her seemed to be amused.

Hilda looked away quickly and her fingers flew with the knitting needles, thinking she must look rather foolish seeming to grin at nothing. Yet, in some perverse way, the impression she gave tickled her own sense of humour.

The staff of Rippon's Plant Hire would be amazed if they knew the super-efficient Miss McAllister could smile, knit — and wind a baby! She knew very well that their nickname for her was "The Robot."

But her eyes were so tired . . . Hilda stopped her furious knitting and laid the garment on the table in front of her, then put her head back against the seat, letting the lids droop to rest them.

Suddenly, through a heavy curtain of sleep, she became aware of someone gently shaking her arm.

"Excuse me, this is where I must get off." The male voice apologised pleasantly.

Hilda blinked and raised her head. It was a moment before she knew where she was, and another before she realised with horror that she had been sleeping with her head on this young man's shoulder. She stammered an embarrassed apology.

He squeezed passed her, grinning at her discomfiture.

"Don't apologise." He laughed. "There were compensations — your hair smells nice, and tastes almost as good." He pretended to pull a long hair from his mouth, then with a chuckle he lifted his case and was gone.

With a start Hilda heard the porter calling out the name of the station, her own destination. She grabbed all her luggage, stuffing her knitting into her bag, then struggled off the train and stood there, feeling disorientated and very little like a computerised robot.

Tiredness enveloped her and all she wanted at that moment was to get into her hotel room, lock the door and go to bed. Yet, it had been fun to sit up to the early hours this morning and listen as her sister, Liz, gave a hilarious account of her holiday in the sun of Tenerife. But not quite so amusing when Baby Martin then woke twice in the night after Hilda had volunteered to keep him in her room for her last night.

HILDA came out of the station now and shuddered a little as a gust of wind with an icy edge greeted her. She tried to hail a taxi, but it was difficult with both hands full, and before she knew what was happening, her knitting, snapshot wallet and purse cascaded from her raised arm. She groaned — she'd forgotten to fasten the zip of her bag.

"Does your mother know you're out by yourself?" a wearily-humorous male voice asked, as he helped to retrieve her belongings. He gasped as the photographs of her nieces and nephews fell out of the wallet.

"Are you a children's nurse?" he asked, with a smile.

"No, they're my relations," she answered, feeling more and more embarrassed.

A taxi drew up beside them and Hilda grasped the handle. This was no time to go into a long-winded explanation of how her parents, both widowed, each with two children, before their second marriage, had then had Hilda and Liz.

People were always amused, so she seldom explained. It made it easier at work to be thought of as an efficient career woman.

"Actually, this is my cab," the young man pointed out, as Hilda struggled to open the door. "But don't start apologising — perhaps we can share it. Where are you going?"

"The River Park Hotel," she stammered. "I've never been here before so I don't know if it's on your way."

"Well, you can't go there," he declared. "It burned down last week!"

Hilda stared at him in disbelief. She had received no cancellation of her booking and suddenly, what with the wind, her tiredness, being in a strange city, and with a new branch office accounts to audit, her eyes became moist. It was all a bit too much!

"Look, just get in," he said. "I know where you can get lodgings for tonight at least." He bundled her into the back of the taxi and slung her luggage in with his, glancing at her name on the label.

"Miss McQueen, 4 Hansford Road," he instructed the driver, who nodded and was soon threading out into the busy city traffic.

It wasn't long before they drew up in front of a pleasant detached house with a neat garden in front. Hilda meekly followed as the young man strode up the path, carrying her luggage.

The door opened before they reached it, and a severe-looking middle-aged woman stood on the doorstep, arms folded, with a honey-coloured cat at her feet.

"No, Fraser Scott, I'm not taking in another of your lame dogs," she declared, before he got a chance to speak.

"But, Kirsty, it's more of a lame kitten this time!" Fraser spoke cheerily, turning to include Hilda.

The cat was now purring ecstatically round Hilda's legs, and it occurred to Hilda how dishevelled she must appear to the older woman. She knew her hair, which was hanging loose, was getting plastered close to her head.

"May I introduce Hilda McAllister?" Fraser smiled broadly to Kirsty McQueen. They were obviously very old friends.

"Well, Hilda, since Tiddles seems to like you, you'd better come in!" Kirsty held the door open wide.

Hilda hesitated, not quite sure if she was really welcome.

"Really, I . . . I could go to a hotel," she stammered.

"Rubbish!" Miss McQueen said decisively. "You need looking after."

Hilda felt herself being propelled into a comfortable sitting-room where a television set was switched on.

"Just take off your wet things and sit down." Miss McQueen pointed to a chair. "I'll away up and put sheets on the bed. And you, Fraser Scott, make yourself useful and carry up the luggage." She hurried out of the room and made her way upstairs.

DAY BY DAY

TALE of a kitchen table. A family feeds round it; on it the housewife bakes and irons. It carries the scores and scars of rough usage; often wiped but never polished.

Tale of an antique table – work of a master craftsman. With skill and endless patience he made it.

Now a rare heirloom, it bears the deep gloss of the years of assiduous care.

Tale of Christ's Gospel. The great Master Craftsman of words. They have been studied and cherished and loved, till the years have brought them the polished glory of something precious and rare.

But the words He spoke are for daily, common use.

Like a kitchen table!

Rev. T. R. S. Campbell.

What was she doing in this strange house, Hilda asked herself, sinking thankfully into the comfortable chair. Then the cat sprang up lightly and landed in her lap, circled twice, and sank down, purring happily.

Hilda laughed weakly to herself, thinking there was something quite pleasant about being thought helpless for a change. She gazed at the many photographs displayed around the room.

"Folks who have stayed with Kirsty," Fraser Scott's voice explained from behind as if he had read her thoughts.

Kirsty appeared in the doorway.

"And if you've got one to spare I'll be glad of it. It's cheery to see familiar faces when you live alone — even his!" Kirsty lifted a snapshot of Fraser as a boy.

"I'm going home!" Fraser stood up in mock annoyance. "There should be a law against neighbours shattering the image of a man-about-town in front of personable young ladies!"

"Ay, your mother will be wondering why you've brought a young lady to my door," Kirsty said. "And she'll be wondering what's keeping you."

"I can take a hint, Kirsty McQueen." He grinned. "But I'll be in later, Hilda, just to see she's treating you well." Then with a wave and a chuckle he went out.

"Grand lad!" Kirsty said. "His mother would like to see him settled with a nice lass."

"Oh, I only just met him on the train," Hilda was quick to explain.

"Is that so?" Kirsty looked surprised. "Well, I think he's fair taken with you," she remarked candidly.

Yet, despite her forthright manner, Hilda found Kirsty McQueen an almost soothing person to be with, for she was a good listener, too.

Hilda surprised herself by explaining how much she missed her parents now they had retired to the South of England. And telling Kirsty in detail, too, the details of her family — the four half-brothers and sisters, and Liz, her full sister, born two years before herself.

"They're all married," Hilda explained. "They call me the maiden aunt! I stand in at holiday times with their children."

"Ay, I've done a bit of that in my time. I was the unmarried one of a family of six." Kirsty shook her head. "But you're too young to be called a maiden aunt."

A N hour later Hilda crawled into bed and gave a sigh of appreciation as the warmth from the electric blanket enfolded her limbs, which were almost trembling now from fatigue.

She felt nicely relaxed after the hot bath and the plate of home-made broth Kirsty had insisted she sup. Somehow she felt she'd known Kirsty all her life.

A hotel was never like this, she thought, as sleep crept over her.

Her last waking thought was that it would have been nice to have waited up till Fraser Scott came. He was such a straight, forthright kind of person, while she so often felt in a turmoil, living two lives at once. The kind aunt always on call to watch her nieces and nephews, and the unfeeling career woman.

Next morning, almost precisely at seven o'clock, Hilda stirred into wakefulness. She stared round the room, at a loss for a moment, then she smiled, remembering her exhaustion of yesterday.

It was the only reason she would ever have consented to staying here, she mused, pleasant though it was. Hotels, especially large ones where she usually went, were anonymous places and she preferred her business life to be like that, with no kind of emotional or personal involvement.

She had enough of that with all her flamboyant close relatives, who were inclined to drain her.

Yet Kirsty was nice, she told herself. She'd always longed for someone to whom she could confide her hopes and fears.

But then resolutely Hilda got out of bed. She would never get through the day if she allowed her thoughts to ramble on in this fashion.

Hilda spent her usual fifteen minutes making up her face so that she would not have to re-touch it for the rest of the day. Then carefully she arranged her hair, wanting to look smart for her one day in this branch office doing a mini audit of the books and accounts.

Then she brought out the train timetable to check up on her train farther north later in the day. And in an orderly fashion she began to check her notes on her firm's local branch. She was just about to read the staff report when there was a knock on the door and Kirsty came in, carrying a cup of tea. She looked at Hilda in frowning amazement.

"You're looking very elegant, quite a difference from last night," she said, almost as though she were disappointed. "Your breakfast will be ready in five minutes, so come down when you've finished your tea so that it doesn't spoil."

"I only take . . ." Hilda began, but Kirsty was out of the room again.

Somehow she couldn't hurt Kirsty by not eating the bacon and egg, placed before her with a flourish — it was only for this once.

Hilda felt a hypocrite when she said goodbye to Kirsty, agreeing to her pressing invitation to come to stay next time she was in the area and to remember to send a photograph.

"I'm not sure if I'll be coming here again," Hilda said, trying to be strictly honest.

"You'll be back, no doubt about it!" Kirsty said with complacent conviction, waving to Hilda as she went down the front path escorted by Tiddles the cat.

THE warmth of her send-off moved Hilda, especially when she knew of the probable hostility which would await her when the staff of the branch arrived and found her already there going through the books.

The atmosphere was usually chilly because her presence was resented and sometimes she wished secretly that the branches were given advance warning of her arrival.

This time, though, somehow staying with the warm-hearted Kirsty had prevented her from affecting her usual formal attitude, and when she arrived at the office it surprised her to find it already open for business. Usually, arriving early, she opened up with her own set of keys.

Hilda pushed open the swing-doors and saw two men standing together, studying a business manual. She hesitated — usually she just walked into the main office and started to work.

As she stood there one of the men sensed her presence and turned round.

She stared in amazement as she recognised the familiar features of Fraser Scott.

"Good morning. I'll be with you in a minute." His quick glance had registered a degree of surprise, too, but he immediately turned back to continue his discussion with the older man.

Hilda opened her briefcase and quietly brought out the notes on staff. Yes, there was Fraser Scott's name, not long promoted.

Normally she would have had this information at her fingertips, but with Kirsty's cheerful chatter during breakfast there had been no time to memorise staff names, Hilda's usual habit.

Now she quickly glanced through the rest of the notes. Besides Fraser, there were only an assistant manager, a cashier and two typists.

"So you *are* the auditor," Fraser remarked, as he saw the firm's headed notepaper in her hand. "Just as Kirsty said you were.

"Thank goodness it's you!" he exclaimed. "They were telling me yesterday in the head office about a female nicknamed The Robot, who strikes terror into all the staff."

He put an arm round Hilda's shoulders and drew her into the working office behind the reception counter.

Then the door opened and a slight, pretty girl came running in, concern on her face as her glance immediately went to the clock.

"What, Alice!" Fraser turned and grinned as he saw her. "Only ten minutes early!"

The girl looked at him and smiled, and the tension in her face disappeared as she looked at him.

As he guided Hilda towards the accounts files, Fraser spoke softly.

"Alice is the main reason I'm so glad it's you who has come for the audit. She's a great worker — efficient, neat and accurate — but she's very sensitive and gets upset easily."

Hilda felt an unexpected flicker of disappointment. He was so genuinely concerned, and she had seen the look Alice had given him. Was there some kind of bond between these two? Yet, what if there was? It was no concern of hers. But she was suddenly aware that Faser Scott had, in some strange, indefinable way, penetrated her strict emotional defences.

"I know where everything is if you need help," Alice offered shyly, a few minutes later.

Hilda smiled and quietly accepted her offer, though normally she would have formally declined. Perhaps it was because she saw something of herself in the shy, anxious-to-please Alice, but that was

A Wondrous Sight

NOW God be praised that I can see again
The beauty of my garden after rain,
After so many days confined to bed,
To see each rosebud lift its sparkling head,
And watch the wagtail strut across the grass,
And trees that bow their heads as breezes pass;
The cushat doves murmur their greeting soft
While clouds like ghostly galleons sail aloft.
The westward sun peeps o'er the garden wall
And lightens up my hollyhocks so tall.
Then Lady Moon reveals her lantern bright
To keep watch o'er my garden, through the night.

Constance McKay.

before she learnt to hide behind the impersonal façade.

Quietly Hilda settled to work, and she had to admit she had seldom seen accounts so neatly kept. No wonder Fraser Scott didn't want his cashier upset.

But later in the morning she frowned down at the large loose-leaf book in front of her — there seemed to be a big discrepancy, the thing she dreaded most.

Fraser was at her side immediately.

"Something wrong?" he murmured. "The look on your face suddenly became tense, almost apprehensive."

"Oh, it's just that some of these figures don't agree," she said, oddly pleased that he had noticed the change in her expression.

"I don't want Alice worried unnecessarily, so let's sort things out right away." His reply quickly quelled her pleasure.

It didn't take long to find the error, a switched figure, and Hilda easily put things right. She watched as Fraser then teased Alice about incompetence, and the other girl coloured prettily.

So it surprised Hilda a little later when Fraser came up to her, carrying two cartons of soup and some sandwiches.

"Come and have lunch in my office," he invited. "Kirsty said I'd to see you didn't skip your midday meal!"

Hilda wondered if Kirsty was a mind-reader. She usually just worked straight through in order to finish quickly and be out of the unfriendly atmosphere of branch offices.

Still, she thought, this office seemed different, everyone accepted Hilda was just doing her job.

During their snack lunch it was mostly business they discussed. She was delighted when Fraser told her he had been promoted again and was taking charge of the firm's northern office. It was one of the firm's plum positions.

In the afternoon she could sense an air of suppressed excitement in the office.

Alice approached her quietly.

"We're giving Fraser a little presentation, although he's only been manager here for six months," she confided. "He's led everyone to believe he's going tomorrow night, but we know he wants to slip off with no fuss tonight. We'd like you to stay on for it."

"I'd love to." Hilda smiled, mentally saying goodbye to her chance of the early train north.

F RASER seemed genuinely touched by the staff's generosity, and accepted the pen and pencil gift set in a strangely subdued manner.

The staff had booked a table at a nearby hotel for dinner later and Hilda was invited along, but she had to refuse.

"I'm due up north tomorrow and I'll have to catch a train this evening," she explained.

"Please come," Fraser urged. "You can drive up with me in the morning."

"My hotel is booked, and I'm not fixed up here for tonight." Hilda didn't want him to be pleasant to her just out of politeness.

"Oh yes, you have." He grinned. "I arranged it last night with Kirsty.

"I planned to take you out for a meal tonight and tell you about a position in my new office I'd like you to apply for." He glanced across the office in mock despair. "But this lot have rather mucked up my plans," he finished.

"What makes you think I want to change jobs?" Hilda looked up at him in surprise.

"While you were tucked up sleeping, Kirsty told me all about you, Hilda," he confessed. "She says you hate being a career woman and she thinks you should be away from your enormous family for a while."

She couldn't help laughing at his answer, thinking how shrewd Kirsty McQueen was. But she glanced over at Alice, all the same, still feeling a little unsure of herself.

Alice caught her glance and walked over to Hilda, accompanied by a tall young man.

"You'll not have met my fiancé, Douglas." She smiled shyly.

Suddenly light-hearted, Hilda smiled back and put her hand out to the young man in a friendly way.

Then Alice dimpled. "We're all hoping you'll come for a meal with us for Fraser's sake. We think he likes you a lot . . ."

"That's what you notice in this office, not a thing passes them." He was grinning broadly.

Suddenly Hilda knew she would go to dinner with them all, and she *would* apply for the new job. Life there wouldn't be dull with Fraser around, she was sure of that.

Hilda had never before felt so attracted to a young man and, she told herself delightedly, it seemed as though the attraction was mutual.

Kirsty McQueen had been quite correct when she had said that she thought Fraser was "fair taken" with Hilda.

The memory brought a smile to Hilda's lips.

What on earth had happened to her "career woman" image, she asked herself. But as Fraser stayed close by her side on the way to the evening out, she knew she didn't need it any more.

They got into the taxi together and she couldn't help giggling merrily at his next words. "But don't go to sleep, I'm starving for my meal!" □

There has been a settlement at Kirkwall, capital of the Orkneys, since prehistoric times, for it is an important site in its well-protected bay. Visitors are attracted to the city, especially to the old town with its twisting streets and Scandinavian-type buildings, clustered around St Magnus's Cathedral. Kirkwall is the only Scottish city with a pre-Reformation cathedral which is structurally undamaged. Earl Rognvald, the then Norse ruler of Orkney, founded it in 1137.

KIRKWALL ORKNEY : J CAMPBELL KERR

The Taming Of Miss Maude

AS she clicked the gate behind her, Susan Lamont turned back for a moment to look at the charming bungalow which she and her older sister, Maude, had bought ten years before.

Until then they had lived with their parents on the outskirts of Glenbowie, but when their parents had both died within a few months of one another, it was Susan who had insisted that they sell their rather large substantial house, and buy the bungalow.

It was a lovely house, Susan thought, as she turned away. At first Maude had refused to consider the idea, but after a while she became interested in the new bungalow built at the end of a cul-de-sac.

Gradually they had come to love the house, and Maude often remarked that it had all been well worthwhile.

Susan sighed as she made for the bus stop which would take her to a more industrialised quarter of their small town. She had an important job as supervisor in a busy workshop turning out soft furnishings.

Maude too had been quite successful in the business world, but she had given up her job in order to nurse their mother in the last sad months of her life.

Later it had seemed natural for Maude to stay at home as housekeeper, while Susan got a job. She sighed, as she thought about her sister.

There was a big gap in their ages — Maude was now past sixty whilst Susan was not yet fifty. She had been too young and immature to fully understand her sister's heartbreak when Maude's young fiancé was killed at the outbreak of war.

by Jean Melville

Often Susan felt that Maude had allowed herself to go a little bit sour, but there had not been a great deal in her life to make her very happy. However, sometimes she was her own worst enemy. Maude's attitude to life often caused arguments between the two women.

And now there was going to be another one, Susan thought, as she walked along High Street and paused for a moment to look in the window of Dixon's hat shop. The beautiful soft pink hat with the tiny bunch of daisies would be so perfect for her wedding . . . if she ever got round to planning it.

TWO years ago Susan had met Andrew Stevenson, a widower with a teenage daughter, when her firm was commissioned to re-curtain a very charming local hotel.

Andrew was an accountant and had been lunching at the hotel with a client when he had literally bumped into Susan. She fell heavily, and he had been most upset, and had called to see her in the workshop to satisfy himself that she was better.

Soon Susan was visiting Andrew's home and meeting his daughter, Julie, and for all three of them, the small semi-detached house which had seemed so bleak since Andrew's wife had died, suddenly became a warm loving home.

Andrew had made no secret of the fact that he was falling in love with Susan, and Julie had watched the romance blossoming with open delight.

When Andrew proposed and was accepted, they had celebrated by cooking a special meal for all three at home. Maude had declined her invitation.

"Your sister should be here, too," Andrew had said as they relaxed in the sitting room, and his eyes were shadowed. On the last occasion he had called at the bungalow for Susan, he had met with a very frosty reception.

Maude had left him in no doubt that she would not approve of any closer relationship between himself and her sister than the most casual friendship.

"We'll just have to give her time," Susan told him. "You see, it was I who persuaded her to give up our old home and to live in the bungalow. If I leave her there by herself . . . she'll be upset."

"But she's a strong, healthy woman," Andrew said, "and you're not depriving her of a home. I don't see why she can't live by herself."

"Because . . ." Susan floundered. How could she explain to Andrew that it was Maude's own nature which was the stumbling block?

At the moment they had one or two friends who called to see them, but they were mainly people whom she had met at evening classes for china painting, or cake icing, or similar pursuits.

Maude did her best, but always she would make an ill-judged remark which was intended to be complimentary, but which turned out to be just the opposite.

O NLY once had Susan seen how this could hurt Maude as she returned one evening from seeing some people off at the gate, to see her sister crumpled up at the fireplace with tears in her eyes.

"Why do I always have to say the wrong thing?" she asked. "I looked at a design for china and remarked that it was in very poor taste, then realised that Miss Welch had chosen it for herself, and was so proud of it. She looked so hurt. Why do you bother with me, Susan?"

"Because you're my sister, and I love you." Susan had tried to console her. "People know you don't mean to be unkind, and sometimes you say things which need to be said."

"They wouldn't come here at all, if it weren't for you," Maude had said, then added. "You are all I have, Susan."

"Nonsense," Susan had said, yet her eyes had clouded. Perhaps there was some truth in this. She had tried to explain it to Andrew but his warm, friendly nature was so different from Maude's.

Yet now as she walked to her job, she knew she would have to talk to Maude sooner or later and tell her that she was to marry Andrew. Susan's heart lurched at the thought. She was not looking forward to seeing the upset in Maude's eyes.

But when Susan did tell her, Maude hid her upset behind anger, then made the mistake of saying that Andrew Stevenson was not good enough for her.

"You mean you would go and live in that poky little house?" she asked. "And be stepmother to a teenage girl? You know what I think about teenagers!"

"I know what you think about everything, Maude," Susan said, goaded. "I've been wondering how to tell you, but now that I've done so, I'm glad. I would like to bring Andrew and Julie to dinner tomorrow night, and I hope you will be friendly towards them, and accept them as new members of the family."

"Never," Maude said. "How can you be so heartless, Susan? What shall I do on my own? How can I manage? You know this house was your choice, and now you are going to leave me here, and I shan't be able to manage by myself."

"We are both quite well off now, after the sale of the old house." Susan reasoned

"Yes, and that man is only after your money!"

Susan's face went chalk white.

"I shall forget that remark, Maude, but if you're unpleasant to Andrew and his daughter tomorrow night, I will be very hurt."

JULIE STEVENSON received her invitation to have dinner at the bungalow the following evening, with mixed feelings. She had met Miss Lamont on more than one occasion and she looked forward to having an evening out, but not if she and her father were made unwelcome.

At one time Miss Maude had not been quite such a difficult woman. Julie remembered her teaching at Sunday school before Mr and Mrs Lamont died and she and Susan moved to the bungalow. But Julie had been only seven then, and no doubt Miss Lamont would seem very different to her now.

She still looked just the same, Julie thought the following evening. But when they were shown into the sitting-room Miss Lamont was very cool and detached.

What a pretty house it was, Julie thought, yet how cold it was with no fun and laughter to warm it up.

Nevertheless, the visit went off without any trouble, but mainly because everyone was careful not to put a foot down wrong.

THE following evening at the youth club, Julie was so preoccupied that she made a very poor opponent for Charles Ferguson at the table-tennis table.

"You're not concentrating," he said. "What's up, Julie?"

She looked up and blushed a little. Charles hadn't been in Glenbowie very long and he hadn't as yet singled out any particular girl for attention, but Julie had hoped, secretly, that he might notice her.

He worked in the County Planning office and wore an air of quiet competence, whatever he was doing.

"I'm sorry," she apologised.

"Can't I help?" He sounded sincere.

She shook her head.

"I doubt it. I . . . I don't suppose you know Miss Maude Lamont?" she asked.

"Not know her!" Charles cried. "That woman is the bane of my life. She spends her days writing letters of complaint and the number of them who find their way on to my desk has to be seen to be believed. Why? Have you had a row with her?"

"No," Julie said, slowly, "but I might."

"Why?" His curiosity was evident. "What are you going to do to her?"

"Ask her to accept me as a lodger," Julie said, simply, trying hard not to grin at the surprise on Charles' face.

"You must be joking!" He was incredulous. "Or mad! Why would you do a thing like that?"

Julie bit her lip.

"Her sister is going to be my stepmother."

Charles reddened.

"Oh dear," he said, "I'm great at putting my foot in it. I'd no idea she was a relative of a sort."

"She isn't . . . yet, and she's all you say she is. But her sister, Susan, is engaged to my father and they are so happy together. I don't want that happiness spoiled, and I'm so afraid of Miss Maude putting a spoke in it." She sighed.

"She'll be left on her own, you see, and although Susan is trying hard to be firm, I wouldn't put it past Miss Maude to make her feel so guilty she might call off the wedding. So I'm going to offer myself as the lodger.

"I'm still training at the Technical College, but I can bus it there as easily from the bungalow as from home. What do you think?"

CHARLES' face was full of admiration as he looked at her. "I think it's very considerate of you, but I'd rather pick you up from your old home when we go out on a date, than from Miss Lamont's," he said, ruefully.

"What date?" she blushed, trying hard not to look too pleased.

"Well, I thought perhaps we could go to the Ice Rink next weekend, that's if you're not busy?" he added hastily.

"No, I'm not, and I'd love to come." Julie laughed, though her face sobered again as she and Charles parted company. She didn't look forward to carrying out her decision to move in with Miss Maude. Then she brightened, at least some good had come of it — her date with Charles.

Julie had a day off the following Tuesday and she reluctantly decided that if she were going to carry out her plan, she must do it on that day.

The prospect of approaching Miss Maude worried her, though.

Susan was still determined that Maude would not spoil her happiness and she had even bought her wedding hat, a soft pink affair with a bunch of daisies on the crown. It wasn't Julie's style at all, but it suited Susan. What kind of hat would Maude buy, she wondered with an inward smile, if a miracle happened and she did come to the wedding.

She was about to slip her old sheepskin coat over her jeans in order to make her way to the bungalow when she paused for thought.

Miss Maude was very old fashioned and would expect to see her dressed up a little. There was no sense in spoiling her chances straightaway.

She found her best pale-green coat, which swung from her shoulders in a wide swirling skirt and which she wore with elegant tan boots and matching gloves.

To say that the older woman was surprised to see her was putting it mildly. Miss Maude's eyes were suspiciously bright and she looked as though she had been crying.

"Please come in," she invited Julie. "I'm just preparing some vegetables for a casserole . . . onions, in fact."

"Oh, I see," Julie said, satisfied.

"Aren't you at school today?" the old woman queried, showing Julie into the sitting-room.

> ## *First Signs*
>
> AUTUMN showed in the wood today!
>   A leaf came floating down,
> Its wrinkled edge with yellow fringed,
>   Its centre tinted brown.
>
> The fruit hung on the crabtree bough
>   All mellow and mature,
> A squirrel searched around for nuts
>   To fill his winter store.
>
> The scarlet hips I noticed there,
>   Where once wild roses grew.
> The briars with their glossy fruit
>   All wet with morning dew.
>
> The elderberry, red and black,
>   And hawthorn, too, I saw.
> And acorns scattered all around
>   About the woodland floor.
>
> *Leonard J. Wells.*

"College. No, we have today free." Julie explained.

"So many holidays these days," Miss Maude muttered, disapprovingly. "It was different when I was a girl Would you . . . er . . . would you care for something to eat?"

"No, thank you," Julie said. "Er . . . perhaps I should tell you why I've come . . . I wanted to ask if you'd take me as a lodger," she said with a rush. "I can't pay much, but I can manage a little, and . . . and you wouldn't need to be on your own when Susan marries my father."

Miss Maude sat down abruptly, her mouth open in astonishment.

"A lodger!" she cried. "You . . . live here? Why . . ."

"I'm not terribly tidy, but I'm quite clean and I could do the cooking occasionally." Julie continued truthfully.

"I go out two nights per week to the youth club and the skating rink. Otherwise I would be at home, so you wouldn't be on your own."

"But I *prefer* to be on my own rather than have the wrong company," Miss Maude said, and watched the ready colour rush to the girl's cheeks.

"Oh, I don't mean *you* so much . . ." the old woman added.

"I think you do mean me," Julie said, quietly. "I'm sorry. It was just an idea."

"No, I mean young people," Miss Maude said. "I can't seem to get on with young people."

"Why? What's wrong with them?" Julie was astounded.

"Wrong!" This time there was no blundering on Miss Maude's part. "I'll tell you what is wrong. Have you seen Glenbowie recently? Have you really looked at the place as you walk along?

"We always took such pride in our town. The parks were well kept, the paths weeded, and there was even a fountain in the square. That had to be turned off six years ago because of abuse."

"Yes, I remember." Julie rose to her feet. "I must say I came here ready to be mad at you if you did not do a swap . . . Susan for me . . . but I can't say I blame you, Miss Maude. I . . . I'm eighteen and one of your teenagers. I hadn't really noticed the vandalism in the town. Somehow one takes it for granted."

"Well, what is the use of lecturing you, poor child?" She sighed. Julie nodded sadly.

"Well, goodbye, Miss Maude," she said. "I'm sorry that . . . that you don't approve of my father for Susan. They really do love one another, you know."

A T the youth club on Friday evening, Julie was still very quiet and thoughtful. Charles had promised to look in, but he was working late and they were going skating on Saturday. Nevertheless he managed a quick visit and laughed when he saw Julie's rueful face.

"Well?" he asked. "So you were turned down. What spoiled your chance?"

"Us," she said, quietly. "All of us. All the hooligans in our town. Oh, I know we are all right individually, but we do have some rough careless people among us, and when they get together in a gang, they don't know where to stop. Have you seen the bus shelter outside? And the telephone box?"

"I know, I know," he acknowledged. "I've read all about it in letters." ·

"Miss Maude has a point," Julie said, truthfully.

"She has several, but I don't know how it is going to be stopped." Charles sighed.

Julie suddenly looked determined.

"I don't think I could even try if it were for myself, but for Susan and my father I'm going to have a go. It's my turn to collect the money tonight, and I'm also going to make a speech."

Charles looked at her, intrigued.

At first there were shouts and calls from some of the boys when Julie rapped on the table with her shoe then stood up on a chair.

"I'm going to make a speech," she called in her clear voice. "Mr Beddows, our leader, isn't here tonight but I'm sure he wouldn't mind my doing it, if he were here.

"We are being accused of ruining this town," she cried, "and I couldn't deny it. Have you all looked at some of the walls? And the broken panes of glass and trampled flower beds?

"If you haven't, then take a good look tomorrow and I vote we meet here on Monday and talk it over." Julie looked around her at the sea of faces.

There was silence and suddenly Julie felt awkward and foolish. It looked as if no-one was even interested. Then she heard Charles' voice.

"Julie's right — I think we should all support her," he cried.

"We're with you, Julie," one or two of the girls shouted, and although the boys were more silent, no one condemned the speech.

As the weeks slowly passed towards the date set for the wedding, Julie asked her future stepmother to take a message home to Miss Maude. The older woman was still proving stubborn, though Julie had spotted her looking in the window of Dixon's hat shop.

"Tell her that the next time she goes to town, can she look at the bus shelter, and can she specially look at the telephone box on the corner of your street?"

"They all look fine to me," Susan said. "In fact, the town is beginning to look quite smart these days. Your father is in the gardening club and he says they may enter Glenbowie for the award for the most attractive small town next year."

"Oh, Dad!" Julie cried. "Is that true? Wait till I tell the youth club. We've all been working like mad on the place."

"I think you young people ought to be thanked publicly," Susan said, as Julie told her the whole scheme. "Everyone must have noticed the difference you've all made."

"No, it is Miss Maude we must thank." Julie said, firmly.

"She is going to be invited to the youth club on Monday night. I think the boys and girls would like to thank her, too."

THE youth club was in full swing on Monday evening when the door suddenly opened and Miss Maude Lamont stood there, clad in a neat navy suit with matching hat.

There was a startled silence, then a great burst of applause as Mr Beddows, the youth club leader, welcomed her and drew her to a small platform at one end of the room.

"I would like to say on behalf of everyone how much we appreciate the way you drew our attention to the very sorry state of our town.

"The young people are taking a great pride in it now, but someone had to point the way, and that someone was you."

"I . . . I hardly know what to say," Miss Lamont said. "I'm well known for my sharp tongue, but for once it seems to have done some good.

"Glenbowie *was* a mess. It is no longer so. I'm very, very proud of it . . . and of you," she ended.

"The young people have bought you this little gift," Mr Beddows went on, handing Miss Lamont a box of chocolates.

"It would have been delivered to you if you had not come this evening, but we are delighted to do it in person, and in fact, to welcome you any time you care to drop in."

"Not if there's the usual loud pop music going," Miss Maude cried tartly. But she had to take a hankie out to wipe away a tear.

"I can only thank all of you very much. These are my favourite chocolates. Now I'll leave you to finish your evening without me."

Miss Lamont stood in the bus shelter and looked at the clean, sparkling windows and fresh paint, then she thought about the girl Julie. Surely she would be Julie's aunt when Susan married Andrew Stevenson? It might be fun to be an aunt.

How could she ever have said she thought Andrew not good enough for Susan? Her cheeks burned at the thought, and at the thought that she had tried to spoil Susan's happiness.

She would not have the girl as a lodger, though. That would not do at all. Julie belonged to Andrew and Susan, not to her, but she could come and visit her often. And there was a rather nice hat in Dixon's window, which was very suitable for a wedding . . .

Miss Lamont looked at her box of chocolates. There was a soft-centred cherry one in there somewhere and she couldn't wait till she got home. She selected the chocolate, the paper sticking a little to her fingers before she managed to free it, then she popped it into her mouth, closing her eyes as she munched it with enjoyment.

Suddenly she was startled as two angry youngsters rushed towards her and thrust her chocolate paper back into her hand.

"Littering up the floor of our bus shelter," said one girl, her blue eyes very bright. "You older people think you can do anything you like, but you'd better tidy up from now on."

Miss Lamont almost choked on her chocolate, then she began to laugh and laugh. Just wait till she told Susan, Andrew and Julie when she invited them all to dinner on Sunday. ☐

Glamis Castle was the childhood home of Queen Elizabeth, the Queen Mother. King Robert II granted the lands of Glamis in Angus to the Lyon family (the Earls of Strathmore) in 1372. Fragments of a 14th-century building are thought to be incorporated in the present-day castle. It was Patrick Lyon, first Earl of Strathmore, who had the castle rebuilt in the French chateau style in the 17th century. The castle is open to visitors and is situated near the town of Kirriemuir.

GLAMIS CASTLE ANGUS : J CAMPBELL KERR

Ticket To Happiness

by ELIZA YEAMAN

AILEEN MURRAY came hurrying through the swing doors and dumped an enormous cardboard box at the side of the lift.

Her cheeks were pink with her exertions and there was a sprinkling of snow in her dark hair.

Fred Rattray, who was the doorman on early shift, thought that she looked as pretty as a picture. If it had been any of the other girls who worked in the building, he would have told her so.

But Aileen's formal good morning was cool, almost as frosty as the December morning. Fred smiled, though, as he answered her, and to his astonishment she smiled back at him. He was almost dazzled by the brilliance of her smile, by the unexpected radiance which lit her face for a moment.

"I've another box to come," she told him, as she turned back to the swing-doors and ran out to the car park.

By the time she returned, Fred had manoeuvred the first box into the lift. "Decorating the office this year again, Miss Murray?" he asked her jovially.

The second box was open and he could see that it was filled to capacity with holly branches, the scarlet berries gleaming among the glowing shades of green.

"Yes, decorating again." Aileen looked at the clock. "I've given myself exactly an hour before the others arrive."

Fred's gaze followed hers to the clock. Yes, she had timed herself as precisely as that, he noticed. Every year she did the same. He knew that in an hour's time the office would be transformed into a Christmas wonderland.

"It doesn't seem long since last Christmas," Fred found himself saying. "The year has just flown by."

Miss Murray pursed her lips as if in disagreement with his remark. But she answered him amiably enough. "Yes, time flies, they say, Fred."

Already her finger was pressing the button for the second floor and the lift doors were closing. "If you want any help, give me a call." He smiled obligingly.

Aileen's answer came swiftly. "I won't need any help, thanks!"

TYPICAL, Fred thought, typical. These independent modern girls! He frowned disapprovingly as he picked up his morning paper and resumed reading. Then he put the paper down again abruptly.

Last year at this time, he realised, he hadn't been in the least critical of Miss Murray. In fact, he would go so far as to say that he admired her. Often he thought that some of the other girls could well take a leaf out of her book. She wasn't only punctual and efficient, she was also extremely sensible and invariably pleasant to everyone.

Funny how your attitude towards someone could change so completely in the short space of a year, Fred thought. Less than a year in fact, more like six months, he calculated. At the same time he had a clear picture in his mind of Steven Rankine, the young accountant who had joined Harper & Mutch's last May.

Anyone with half an eye could see that Steven Rankine had fallen for Miss Murray in a big way, Fred's thoughts ran on. Too much alike, that's what they are.

"Can I offer you a lift?" Steven had asked her, away back in the summer when he was still new to the firm.

"Thanks — I've got transport." Miss Murray's reply had been amiable and yet firm. And, of course, she'd walked out without a backward glance.

"Can I buy you some lunch?" Steven had asked, another day.

"I go home for lunch, thank you all the same." She had smiled kindly enough, but she hadn't waited to see his downcast expression.

No doubt there had been other conversations which Fred hadn't had the privilege of overhearing. Then again, maybe not. For only last week he had heard Steven offering to help Miss Murray to carry some parcels. And, naturally, her reply had been cool and decisive: "I can manage, thank you."

Stubborn fools, the pair of them, Fred thought to himself. Couldn't that clever Mr Rankine see that in order to make any headway with a girl like Miss Murray, he would have to relinquish his gallant "I'm-a-superior male" attitude? Or couldn't she, just for once, pretend to be just a little less competent?

Impatiently, Fred rustled his newspaper as his eyes returned to the headlines. It was none of his business. He had seen hundreds of romances blossoming in the building during his twenty-two years as a doorman.

Some had flourished and some had perished. Noticing things was part of his job, in a way. He took a friendly, fatherly interest in all the various comings and goings. But never before had he been so tempted to become involved.

Perhaps it was because he knew instinctively that these two young folk were desperately lonely. If only they would come down from their lofty pedestals — or if one of them would — they would discover how right they were for each other. Couldn't one of them realise it, Fred asked himself.

SIMILAR thoughts were stirring surreptitiously in Aileen Murray's mind as she fixed decorations and greenery all round the office.

On Friday night when Steven had asked her if she had anything special planned for the weekend, she had told him briskly that, yes, she had a whole list of things to do.

In her heart, she had known that his question was the prelude to offering to take her out. If I say I'm doing nothing, he'll chivalrously rescue me from boredom, she thought stubbornly.

It was always like that. Every time Steven made the slightest approach to Aileen, she deliberately threw up a barrier. She didn't know why — it just happened. And, afterwards, she regretted it.

Sometimes she wished that Steven Rankine had never come to work in the office.

If she'd never met him, she reflected, her life would be much simpler and less complicated.

You mean much more dull and absolutely colourless, Aileen scolded herself. While she was alone, she allowed herself to think in these terms. But whenever she and Steven came face to face, a blaze of antagonism flared up inside her head.

At least, it had been antagonism at first. Gradually, though, when she found her thoughts dwelling on him endlessly, repeating their brief conversations over and over, she began to know that Steven had a compelling fascination for her.

Only it was too late. Her constant, persistently cool rejections had made him wary, and he seldom spoke to her at all in the office. When he did, he had the air of someone on guard, ready to catch the words which would be thrown back at him.

Yes, Steven reminded her of a cricketer. Tensely, he would run up and throw the ball and inevitably she would bat it away as far as she could. Out of play, she mused, so that the game was over before it was properly begun.

But it isn't a game, she told herself as she hurriedly finished her self-imposed task, then pushed the empty boxes into the stationery cupboard. She mustn't start day-dreaming again. Courage was what she needed; the nerve to put one of these tickets inside the Christmas card she had bought for Steven.

Aileen visualised the scene in the office on Christmas Eve — everyone would be opening their presents. Steven would look at the ticket, and when he turned his quizzical gaze to her, she would say, "I bought one for myself as well."

No, no, she couldn't go through with it! Aileen shuddered at the very idea.

At lunch-time today she would go out and buy a box of handkerchiefs for him, the same kind as she had bought for Mr Harper, her boss. She had never bought anything on impulse before, certainly not anything as expensive as the two tickets for the *Messiah*.

EVERLASTING JOY

CHRISTMAS EVE! Great singing over midnight. In the darkness of the land, a thousand lighted Churches; multitudes come forth to swell the Christmas chorus. Singing from the heart the old beloved hymns of star and shepherds, of Wise Men and the Wonder Child.

Turning Bethlehem's immortal tale into one mighty choral song. Why sing at Christmas? The heart alone can tell, for it lifts to God's great promise: Peace shall be on earth when man shall practise goodwill, through Christ, His Redeemer Son.

Such tidings of comfort and of joy must set the heart a-singing. God's promise aye endureth; the heart shall ever lift with joy.

Raise then the midnight song of Christmas,
song that will never die!

Rev. T. R. S. Campbell.

In the music shop, while she was choosing a record for her nephew, she had noticed a poster advertising the concert, and at the time buying the tickets had seemed like an inspired notion. Now she knew that it was the silliest idea she'd ever had. Her early-morning hopes dissolved abruptly . . .

Almost angrily, Aileen stared around the brightly-festooned office. Christmas was surely a time for being brave! Why did she have to be so timid and hesitant?

The staff began to arrive in the office; Debbie and Gillian were first and their exclamations of surprise and delight soon brought a smile to Aileen's lips. It was a pleasure to see their faces lighting up, to see the Monday morning gloom disappearing from their eyes.

But she was looking away from the door by the time Steven entered and she missed seeing his first reaction to the transformation she had wrought.

During the coffee break, he mentioned it, though, and for once Aileen accepted his compliments with a smile.

"I always do it — it's a sort of tradition." Suddenly, she found herself wanting to tell him about that first Christmas after she had lost her parents. Alone in her tiny flat, she had dreaded the prospect of Christmas. What was the point of putting up the decorations she had brought from her parents' house? There would be nobody to see them.

Aileen had lain awake, thinking about the magic of Christmas, longing to see the decorations hung up. And then the idea had come to her — she would take them into the office! After all, her life was her work, her colleagues were her friends . . .

Then she realised with a start that Steven was talking to her, asking if they had any other traditions. Was there an office party, for instance?

"Not really a party," Aileen answered, blushing as she continued. "We usually just exchange a few little presents during the afternoon tea break on Christmas Eve."

"Will you come shopping with me?" Steven's muttered question was a plea from his heart. "I've no idea what to buy!" He gazed at her in appeal. "And I'm hopeless at wrapping up parcels!"

"Yes, I'll help if you really want me to." Aileen smiled. "But, honestly, it's not necessary. I'm sure nobody would notice."

Steven put his coffee cup down on the trolley, frowning before he replied.

"Oh, they would all notice," he declared. There was a long pause before his features lifted into a smile as he looked at her.

Aileen was aware of a distinct and delicious fluttering of her heartbeat as she waited for him to go on.

"And besides," his eyes glinted with some secret amusement, "I rather like the idea of presents."

Fred Rattray noticed the young couple as they went out together, and the sight of them warmed his heart. Who would have thought to see Miss Murray blushing like a rose and Mr Rankine holding the door open for her and smiling all over his face?

T HE shopping expedition was an unqualified success. All that Steven needed now was a present for Mr Harper.

"Let's leave that until tomorrow," he suggested. "It's time we had something to eat."

Aileen had definitely decided now to stick to her original idea of putting the concert ticket in with Steven's Christmas card. A mere half an hour of his company had made her wonder why on earth she could ever have wavered in her purpose.

While they enjoyed some tea and sandwiches they also talked non stop, and constantly smiled at each other.

"I'm glad we still have one present to buy," Steven told her. "It means we can do this again tomorrow!"

Aileen nodded, unable to look away from his intense gaze. And as they went out of the café it seemed only natural for him to put his hand on her elbow to guide her towards the door.

Outside on the pavement, he removed his hand and she was sure that her elbow was suddenly cold. Aileen's heart skipped a beat. Her entire being grew cold at the thought of losing him now, just when they were getting to know each other. What if she said the wrong thing again?

For a moment, they were separated by the hurrying crowds of shoppers and she turned her head to look at him as he came back to her side.

Steven smiled at her, as if to reassure her of his presence. She smiled back at him and then she looked away, her heart beating nervously, uncertainly.

They were walking past a dress shop and Aileen stopped for a moment to admire a dress, and then glanced at her watch.

"Did you want to buy the dress?" Steven asked.

"Yes, but it's too late," Aileen answered. "I'll have to come back at five o'clock." Then with a final look at the dress, she told him as they began to walk on, "I always like to buy something new for Christmas."

S OMETHING new for Christmas," Steven repeated, and they exchanged another lingering smile before he solemnly spoke.

"That's like us, isn't it, Aileen? We're starting something new for Christmas, aren't we?" He grinned happily.

"I'd like to think so . . ." She had to swallow hard before she could answer, and her voice was shaky and quite unlike her own.

Steven moved his carrier bag of parcels to his other hand as he searched in his pocket and brought out two tickets.

"I bought these on Saturday hoping to find the courage to ask you to come with me." He held them out to her.

"I'd love to go with you," she said happily. As their gaze met and held, she had an irresistible urge to tell him about the concert tickets she herself had bought. It was as if she wanted to share her whole world with him.

"It's like a miracle, isn't it?" Steven said in amazement, when she opened her bag and produced the tickets to show him. "Fancy both of us buying tickets for the same concert!"

An air of enchantment seemed to envelope them as they gazed happily at each other.

When they eventually got back to the office and walked through the swing doors, the tickets were still in Aileen's hand.

Her eyes lighted on Fred, the doorman, who greeted them with a beaming smile. Impulsively, Aileen put the two tickets in his hand.

"Christmas present for you, Fred," she said. "Merry Christmas!"

"Compliments of the season, Fred," Steven chimed in, with an enormous grin.

"Thank you very much," he called after them. "And a Merry Christmas to you both!" But he knew perfectly well that they neither heard him nor saw him. They only had eyes for each other. □

Live And Let

by ELSIE JACKSON

PAULINE ANDERSON, racing across Glasgow's Central Station, was quite oblivious of the heads that turned to give her an admiring glance.

The tall brunette saw only that the Seacots train was preparing to move off, and that the ticket collector was waving her frantically through the barrier.

By the time she leapt into the already-moving train and collapsed on to a seat, she was completely breathless, and her legs felt like jelly. It had been a near miss, for the train she'd caught from Euston had been running almost twenty minutes late.

"May I put that up on the rack out of your way?" The sun-tanned young American sitting opposite Pauline indicated the suitcase she had dumped in the passageway.

"Please!" Pauline gasped, smiling gratefully at the young man.

Then, as the American's eye fell on the label on the front of her case, Pauline saw his eyebrows shoot up.

"Kerrison Quadrant, Seacots!" he exclaimed. "Well, that's a co-incidence! That's where I'm heading for myself. I'm aiming to spend a month with my relatives there, before I move south to London."

"And I've just come from London!" the dark-haired girl answered, as the young man settled back down in his seat. "I've been working there as a computer programmer for three years, but the firm folded up. So, after a short holiday, I'm starting in a job back up here."

"In Seacots?" He smiled enquiringly.

"Oh, no!" Pauline's laughter rippled through the near-empty compartment. "Seacots is too small for big firms or computers. I'll be working in Glasgow, and travelling from home every day.

"I'm Pauline Anderson, by the way," she added, extending a hand, to have it gripped firmly by her companion, who introduced himself as Darren McKinlay.

Normally when Pauline came up to Seacots from London she found this last lap of the journey tedious. On this particular Friday evening, though, the train seemed to be jet propelled.

Darren, a graphic designer from California, soon had her listening to his fascinating tales of his life back in the States, and Pauline was astounded when she looked out and saw that they would soon be pulling into Seacots Station.

"Journey's end!" She smiled to Darren, getting to her feet.

But the blond young man rose smartly to anticipate her, by handing down her heavy case. Then he swung down his own lightweight hold-all.

"Is that all your luggage?" Pauline asked in amazement.

"I'll equip myself as I go along." Darren smiled. "I'm hoping to settle over here, you see, to start my own business."

Then, as the train started to slow down, he glanced a shade diffidently across at the girl.

"I wonder . . . do you think we could get together some evening?" he suggested. "Go out for a meal, perhaps? Since we're almost going to be neighbours!"

"That would be lovely," Pauline said warmly, holding tightly to her seat as the train jolted along by the platform.

"What about next Tuesday evening, then?" Darren suggested. "I expect our respective folk will have seen enough of us by that time. They won't mind us having an evening out."

"FINE!" Pauline agreed, her brown eyes shining. "By the way, where exactly in the Quadrant are you staying, Darren?" she asked, as they started along the corridor to leave the train.

"Number 96," the young man told her. "With the Dows. Mrs Anne Dow's my dad's young sister, and Colin's the only male cousin I have in the world.

"He and I are great buddies — he came over to visit us in California last year. But perhaps you know them?" he asked, springing lightly down on to the platform. He set Pauline's case down, then put a protective hand beneath her elbow as she jumped down from the step.

"Yes, I do." Pauline's cheeks had become warm all of a sudden. There was an anxious expression in her brown eyes as she caught sight of the trio who were coming purposefully across the platform towards Darren.

" 'Bye, then!" she said hastily, lifting her case and hurrying off towards the car park entrance. She could see her father standing waiting for her.

"Just a minute, Pauline!" Darren came bounding after the girl to grip her arm. "About Tuesday!" He grinned. "We didn't settle on a time. Will seven o'clock be OK?" He rushed on. "I'll be hiring a car, so I can pick you up — Number 35 Kerrison Quadrant, isn't it?" He certainly had been observant.

"Yes, that's right. Fine!" Pauline assured him, still retreating. "I must dash now," she said, a trifle breathlessly. "My dad's waiting."

"Sure." Darren relinquished the grip on her arm and raised his hand in a gesture of farewell. He turned to hurry back and greet his relatives, who were now standing stock still beside the young man's hold-all.

Even from the distance Pauline could see the dismayed expressions on their faces.

Honestly, she thought, as she continued on her way. She had been so looking forward to a tranquil break before starting her new job, then something awkward like this had to happen! It was all so stupid and unnecessary, too, that was what really annoyed her!

"Hello, love! Good journey?" Leonard Anderson strode forward, arms wide, to receive his elder daughter.

"Fine, Dad." Pauline returned his hug warmly. As her father took her case from her, she tucked an arm smilingly in his.

Live And Let Live

IT wasn't until eleven o'clock that night, when she was alone in her room, that Pauline had leisure to reflect upon her predicament.

For over three hours the tongues of the Anderson family had wagged non-stop, yet not once had Pauline mentioned her meeting with Darren McKinlay, or her forthcoming date with him — not even when she was chatting alone in the kitchen to her young sister, Laura.

And why, she asked herself. All because of some stupid neighbours' quarrel that had happened when she was a mere toddler!

The girl moved restlessly over to the window, pulled back the curtains, and looked down on the square of tidy, semi-detached houses with neat little gardens. For youngsters the Quadrant had been an ideal playground with very little traffic.

"And don't you be going into the Dows' garden to play, now, we don't want anything to do with that family!" Pauline could still hear her mum's voice. Freckle-faced Craig Dow, two years older than Pauline, had obviously been issued the same warning regarding the Andersons.

Although Pauline, Laura and Craig had joined in the same communal games, they had only exchanged words when strictly necessary. Pauline had often wondered about this animosity between the families, but had never dared broach the subject to her parents.

Mrs Anderson's normally smiling lips would tighten at the very mention of the Dows, Mrs Dow in particular.

Pauline moved away from the window now and sat down in front of the dressing table. She was twenty-one, a career girl and independent, with a mind of her own. She didn't want any part of a stupid neighbours' quarrel, she told herself. The sooner her family appreciated that fact the better!

Nevertheless, she found herself tiptoeing into Laura's room ten minutes later to ask her young sister a favour.

Laura's eyes widened when Pauline told her about Darren McKinlay, and how she had arranged to go out with him.

"Would you break the news to Mum, Laura?" she asked, flushing. "I think it'll be easier that way."

"I suppose so," she agreed. "It's so silly, grown-up folk acting like children. I've often seen Craig looking as though he'd like to break the ice, too."

"Did Mum ever mention the cause of the quarrel, Laura?" Pauline asked curiously, perching cross-legged on the end of her sister's bed.

"No, Mum's ever so funny about it, but she and Mrs Dow were great friends before it happened."

"Well, whatever the cause," Pauline eased herself off the bed, "neither Darren McKinlay nor I had anything to do with it. And I hope Mum, and Dad, too, will have the good sense to see that."

Lenny and Sylvia Anderson did see Pauline's point of view, even though it took them a couple of days to get used to the idea.

When Darren McKinlay appeared promptly at the door on Tuesday evening and was ushered into the living-room by Pauline, no-one could have been more charming.

When they finally set off in Darren's hired car, though, Pauline was aware of a great sense of relief.

"Well, that went off all right, anyway!" She spoke her thoughts aloud.

"Oh, I'm used to mixing." Darren grinned. "I do a lot of designing for industry, you know — packages, advertisements — I'm not a head-in-the-clouds arty type."

"It wasn't you I was worrying about . . ." Pauline began, and by the time they had arrived at the Cockleshell Restaurant, Darren had learned the reason for her remark.

"I did think Aunt Anne and Uncle Finlay were acting kind of funny!" Darren chuckled. "I couldn't figure it out. And Craig kept looking like he was going to say something, only he never did."

"It's all so crazy!" Pauline declared. "Holding a grudge all these years is such a waste of time." She was gazing out of the restaurant window at the sun setting over the sea.

"Yes, I know what you mean," Darren said, following her gaze. "All this beauty in the world, and people will insist on making ugliness."

The meal of roast duck, followed by lemon soufflé, matched the view in perfection, and when they finally left for home Pauline was fairly glowing with contentment.

The Messengers

AIMLESSLY I walked into my garden —
Black and cold and cheerless was
the ground —
Nothing could be growing yet, I
reasoned . . .
Then, to my delight and joy, I found
Green swords through the hard and
bare earth peeping . . .
Winsome snowdrops waking from
their sleeping!

Such enchanting messengers . . .
they bring
All the fresh new hope and joy of
SPRING.

Elsie Campbell

"I've really enjoyed myself, Darren!" she exclaimed impulsively as they drove up Hill Street towards the Quadrant.

The blond young man turned to smile at her. "I was hoping the evening wasn't quite finished yet," he said.

"What do you mean?" Pauline looked at him questioningly.

"I'd like you to come in and say hello to my aunt and uncle, and to Craig," he announced. "It seems such a shame they've missed out on you all these years!" His voice was very sincere.

"Oh, I couldn't, Darren!" Pauline was taken aback. "I'd be so embarrassed!"

"And who was going on about this being a crazy state of affairs?" Darren asked quietly, his blue eyes looking reproachfully down at Pauline.

"All right." She sighed. "I give in, Darren. But I must say I feel as though I'm heading for the lions' den."

Live And Let Live

FIVE minutes later, though, as she sat sipping tea by the Dows' cheery fire, all Pauline's misgivings had completely vanished.

After her initial surprise, plump little Mrs Dow had gone out of her way to be pleasant. And Mr Dow's face had lit up the moment Darren had brought Pauline into the living-room.

Craig, too, who had been over in the corner listening to a tape-recorder, had sprung up, his freckled face wreathed in smiles.

They really are glad I've broken the ice, Pauline realised. I should have done it years ago, or Laura should have.

"And how did you like living in London, Pauline?" Mrs Dow asked.

"It was fine." Pauline smiled. "I liked my job, and the people I worked with. I didn't much care for the hustle and bustle, though, like fighting my way on to the Tube twice a day — things like that."

"I was surprised when I heard that you'd gone," Craig put in. "It must have taken a lot of courage. You hadn't long left school, had you?"

"No, I was just eighteen," Pauline replied shortly, her cheeks reddening. "And I was very homesick for a long while."

"Yes, indeed! There's nowhere like Scotland!" bespectacled Mr Dow stated firmly, placing his empty cup down on the hearth.

"So why not join Craig and me on our sightseeing programme?" Darren suggested. "Craig's arranging it all. He's taking two weeks of his holiday in my honour, and we're going to try to go somewhere different every day. Would you like that?"

"Well, yes," Pauline replied hesitantly. "But I can't butt in like that, Darren! I might just spoil your fun."

"Rubbish!" Craig put in at once. "You could organise the food for us. A woman's touch would be invaluable."

The following week was great fun for Pauline. The weather was idyllic, and she could have found no better company anywhere than the two cousins.

"I used to spend every holiday cycling round these parts." Pauline smiled reminiscently.

"Yes." Craig nodded. "I used to watch you setting off every year, you and your friends. You looked so happy!"

"I was," Pauline replied. "I love the Highlands."

"Why on earth did you leave us, then?" Craig demanded, with a grin.

Pauline looked dreamily away over the blue loch. "I'd fallen madly in love," she said, after a moment. "Or I thought I had, anyway. His name was Nigel Mayfield.

"I met him when I was on a hostelling holiday in the Highlands. He was a student from London — very good looking and great fun. When we went home we wrote to each other every week for three months."

"Yes?" Craig's grey eyes were attentive and sympathetic.

"Oh, I got into a real old state about him, Craig. Nothing would do but I had to go down to London, too. Mum and Dad were furious because I was only eighteen. But I was convinced that my only chance for happiness lay in London." Pauline's expression saddened.

"And didn't it?" Craig asked, after a moment.

169

"No, I discovered that Nigel already had a very charming fiancée, and was planning to get married quite soon. He never thought he would see me in his life again after the holiday."

"What a rotten thing to happen!" Craig murmured.

"Oh, I don't know." Pauline's eyes brightened. "It made me grow up. I was determined to stick it out down in London, until my broken heart mended, and I managed it."

NO-ONE could be melancholy for long with Darren McKinlay about, Pauline decided, giggling helplessly at the young man's antics as he took his photographs. He was forever playing the clown, yet he had a serious side, too. He'd set his heart on trying to end the bad feeling between the Dows and the Andersons.

"I've discovered what started it off," he had murmured to Pauline that morning, while they were waiting for Craig to come out to the car. "My wicked cousin, when he was four years old, chucked your doll's pram over a hedge and smashed it."

"Are you serious?" Pauline had whispered, staring at him in disbelief.

"That's what Craig told me," Darren informed her, with a twinkle in his eye.

"And that's why our parents haven't spoken for all those years!" Pauline had almost squeaked, finding it very hard to believe.

THE following week, the trio went down to Whithorn, up to the Holy Loch, and then spent a blissful day on the Isle of Arran.

At Wednesday tea-time Sylvia Anderson looked across at Pauline. "I haven't seen you look so fit since your cycling days, my girl! Thank goodness you've decided to come back home."

"It's all right for those that have holidays!" Laura grumbled. "Some of us have just to admire the sunshine from the inside of a stuffy old office! And where are you off to this evening, Sis?"

"I'm just going for a walk along the sea-front with Darren." Pauline smiled. "Craig's otherwise engaged, apparently."

"Oh yes." Laura nodded. "This is his Senior Citizens' night."

"His what?" Pauline looked puzzled.

"Craig goes round the town's senior citizens every second Wednesday evening," Laura informed her. "He attends to any electrical repairs they need done. If it's possible, he does it free of charge, I hear."

"And he never mentioned it!" Pauline exclaimed.

"He wouldn't," Laura replied. "I don't know him all that well, but you can see he'd never blow his own trumpet."

Darren made much the same remark that evening as he and Pauline were walking along the promenade, heads down against the blustery sea breeze.

"I just wish Craig would assert himself a bit more," he remarked.

"Well, as long as he's happy . . ." Pauline started, then she gave a little gasp of pain as a grain of sand blew into her eye.

"Hold on!" Darren took out his handkerchief. "I'm good at this." He very gently eased the sand from her eye and wiped the tears from her cheek.

As Pauline sighed with relief, a horn hooted beside them, and Craig rattled past in his old brown van, en route to his next call.

As the two of them made for home Darren spoke again.

"No trip tomorrow, I'm afraid," he announced. "Something's come up and I've got to go up to the bank in Glasgow and attend to some business."

Pauline was just starting to peg up her washing on Friday morning when Craig Dow came round the corner of the house. He walked slowly along the path to the back garden.

"Hi! How are you this morning?" She beamed at the dark-haired young man. "Did you have many jobs last night?"

"Just a few." Craig smiled, but Pauline thought he looked unusually subdued. "I wanted to talk to you about something," he started. Then his voice tailed off.

"It's about Darren," he went on, hands thrust into the pockets of his navy anorak. "Has he said anything to you about his plans?"

"He did mention he was hoping to settle down in this country," Pauline answered, with a surprised glance at Craig. Unhappily, his grey eyes looked into hers.

"Well, he's changed his plans," he said abruptly. "He's had the offer of a highly-paid job back in California, and he's accepted it. He's going home at the end of the month.

"I thought you should know that," he broke off awkwardly. "I could see you were growing fond of him . . ."

The blood rushed into her cheeks in a crimson tide.

"So you thought you'd put an end to that, Craig, did you?" she demanded in a furious, tight voice.

"When Darren was out of the way and unable to speak for himself — what a nice, cousinly thing to do!"

Craig Dow stared at her for perhaps half a minute. Then he turned on his heel and strode back along the garden path without another word.

ONCE up in her room, Pauline sat down heavily on the end of the bed and closed her eyes. Then, without warning, the tears came.

But the hot, scalding tears weren't being shed for Darren McKinlay. They were for Craig Dow, whose grey eyes had just looked at her in such hurt bewilderment.

"How could I?" she whispered to herself. "How could I say such a nasty thing to him? How could I hurt him like that?"

She recalled now the times when she had been aware of a very different expression in his eyes. One that had been there many times during the past two weeks — a glow, and a softness that had made her heart give an involuntary little leap.

That same tenderness had been there again this morning, when he had come round to try to prevent her being hurt. And she had cruelly thrown all his concern and affection back in his face!

With a final, choky little sob Pauline ran into the bathroom to splash cold water over her face.

Then, without stopping even to pull a jacket over her sweater, she raced downstairs and out along the road.

It was Craig, himself, who opened the door, his eyes widening at the sight of Pauline, breathless and distraught, standing there.

"I've come to say I'm sorry, Craig," she blurted out. "I didn't mean it!

"Come on in, Pauline," he said gently, the smile returning to his lips. "This doorstep's a bit draughty for a long conversation."

"I appreciate what you did this morning," she said quietly. "But there was no need. I like your cousin very much, but I'm certainly not in love with him."

"No?" His face brightened so unashamedly that she laughingly reached out to take his hand.

"Does that mean there's a chance for me, then?" Craig asked, caressing Pauline's fingers gently.

There was no need to answer as she looked into his face with the glow of love in her eyes. The next moment his arms came round her as though they would never let her go.

MRS DOW had made a mid-morning pot of tea for the three of them and Pauline was drinking her second cup when the older woman suddenly looked across at her.

"Has your mum ever said anything to you about our quarrel, Pauline?" she asked. "Do you know how it happened?"

"Darren told me it was because Craig threw my doll's pram over a hedge," she replied, with a faint smile. "But I couldn't quite believe that . . ."

Mrs Dow sighed. "Well that was the start of it, certainly," she said. "But there was a lot more to it than that."

"Tell us, Mum," Craig encouraged his mother.

"Oh, it was all so silly!" Mrs Dow exclaimed. "None of us had much money to spare in those days, young married folk never have. Your mum was expecting Laura." She turned to face Pauline. "I'd given her a pile of Craig's baby-clothes that were like new and she was delighted.

"She said if she added them to your baby-clothes, Pauline, she wouldn't have to buy any new ones."

"But where did my doll's pram come in?" Pauline queried.

"Your mum and dad had bought you that for your second birthday." Mrs Dow smiled. "It was a beautiful one and very expensive. But you were the apple of their eye, after all."

"And I really did throw it over a hedge?" Craig probed.

"Yes, you did, you little scoundrel!" his mother exclaimed. "Mrs Anderson was furious, naturally. And I was mortified — absolutely mortified! That's what made me say that dreadful thing, I suppose."

"What dreadful thing?" Pauline's brown eyes were wide.

OH, it was unforgivable!" Mrs Dow's plump cheeks went crimson. "I told your mum she should have been spending her money on new clothes for her baby, instead of on expensive toys that were too good to play with.

"It was such a mean thing to say," she added, biting her lip. "And I never meant it, you know, I really never meant it!

"Your mum came storming round five minutes later and threw the parcel of Craig's clothes in at the kitchen door. Then it was my turn to be hurt," Mrs Dow went on. "But it *was* my fault," she added. "I always knew that. Often I was on the verge of going round to apologise."

"Well, why not go now, Mum?" Craig suggested gently. "Eleven-thirty on a Friday morning's as good a time as any."

"Do you think I could, Pauline?" Mrs Dow, already half-rising, looked at the girl doubtfully.

"I'm sure of it," Pauline told her warmly. "You go on round now. Craig and I'll come along shortly and see how you're getting on."

After Mrs Dow left, Pauline and Craig washed up the dishes, enjoying the feeling of togetherness that the everyday task gave them.

When half an hour had passed they decided it was time to make tracks for the house along the road, to see how things had turned out. When they passed the window and heard the sound of laughter within, they looked at each other with relief in their eyes. "Well, that's all right, then!" Craig declared, pausing to put an arm round Pauline's waist, and looking down at her with a happy smile.

"Yes." Pauline sighed contentedly. Then she gave a little giggle.

"I've just thought what a lot we'll have to tell Darren," she said, "when he comes back from his day in Glasgow."

"Right enough!" Craig agreed, with one of his comical little smiles. "He'll see there's more to us quiet Seacots folk than meets the eye!"

As if to prove his point, he took his girlfriend into his arms, and kissed her very decisively on the lips. □

Printed and Published in Great Britain by D. C. Thomson & Co. Ltd., Dundee. Glasgow, London and Manchester.